The Psychological Autopsy

A Study of
the Terminal Phase of Life

by

Avery D. Weisman
Robert Kastenbaum

This monograph derives from ongoing research at Cushing Hospital, Framingham, Mass. The project is supported by USPHS Grant MHO-1520.

Community Mental Health Journal Monograph No. 4

Price $2.40

Postage and handling will not be added if payment accompanies order.
Price subject to change without notice.

Copies of this monograph may be ordered from Community Mental Health Journal,
2852 Broadway, New York, N. Y. 10025. Bulk prices are as follows: 5 to 10 copies,
10% discount; 11 to 24 copies, 20% discount; 25 or more, 30% discount.

About the authors . . .

Avery D. Weisman, M.D., is a member of the Department of Psychiatry, Massachusetts General Hospital, and of the Department of Psychiatry of the Harvard Medical School.

Robert Kastenbaum, Ph.D., is Director of Psychological Research, Cushing Hospital, and Lecturer in Psychology, Clark University, Worcester, Mass.

CONTENTS

I INTRODUCTION

The significance of the post-mortem examination as a basic instrument of medical science cannot be overestimated. Without the "post," diseases would be known merely as syndromes, substantiated only by weighty opinions, authoritarian doctrines, and empirical remedies. It is disturbing to contemplate limitations medical science would be contending with today if autopsy methods had not been developed and applied.

However, the somatic autopsy does not answer all the questions. Autopsies do not always disclose the cause of death, nor do they invariably demonstrate why patients die when they do. What people die *with* is not the same as what they die *from*. Anatomical changes are the end effects of disease processes, not the processes themselves. Furthermore, what prompts a person to become ill, enter the preterminal phase, and die at a particular time and in a particular way cannot always be ascribed entirely to a disease process. The final illness is a psychosocial as well as a medical event, in the same way that the person's complete biography is something more than the sum total of medical and nursing notes made during his lifetime.

The pathway along which the somatic autopsy has developed excludes the social context or personal circumstances that prevailed during the final period of life. Psychiatry and the behavioral sciences have not yet developed a comparable method for analyzing the mental and social "remains." Lack of such a method might well be one of the reasons why psychological medicine is still in a Galenical phase. Our knowledge about many key psychosocial factors in illness and death is so fragmentary that there is a strong tendency to fill in the gaps with crude surmises and conjectures and to supplement limited information with unwarranted extrapolations.

The authors have constructed an alternative version of the psychological autopsy method first proposed and developed by Shneidman and his colleagues at the Suicide Prevention Center in Los Angeles (Shneidman & Farberow, 1961). As they conceived it, the primary purpose of the psychological autopsy is to establish the intentionality of people who are victims of accidents, illnesses, poisonings, and other fatalities. By interviewing families and acquaintances of the deceased and reconstructing the life style of the victim, their Death Investigation Team seeks to clarify the degree to which a victim participated in bringing about his own death.

The version of the psychological autopsy under consideration here is a procedure analogous in some respects to the somatic autopsy. While the somatic autopsy maintains a focus upon the final illness, the psychological autopsy emphasizes the preterminal and terminal phases of life in their full complexity—or comes as close to that objective as time, skill, and available information permit. Accordingly, the psychological autopsy, as described below, reconstructs the final days and weeks of life by bringing together every available observation, fact, and opinion about a recently deceased person in an effort to understand the psychosocial components of death.

OBJECTIVES

The psychological autopsy shares three objectives in common with the somatic autopsy: (a) retrospective reconstruction and coordination of information, (b) modification of management and treatment, and (c) contributions to basic research. Adherence to these aims should disclose the differences between what observers think ought to happen in the course of dying and what actually does happen. Although the material presented here is derived from a psychological autopsy series involving a specific population—institutionalized geriatric patients—the autopsy method, with certain modifications, is applicable to a wide variety of populations in many different settings.

CONCEPTUAL ORIENTATION

Theoretical aspects of the psychological autopsy will be considered after presentation of selected observations and findings. However, it might be useful at this point to specify a few of the concepts around which the authors have oriented their investigation.

1. During every phase of the life span, people are potentially vulnerable to medical illness and psychological disturbance. Obviously, this fact does not mean that the entire life span, or any particular segment of it, is intrinsically pathological. Yet there is a strong tendency to define a person as pathological simply because he is dying. In contrast with this view, the investigators hold that the dying process is as "natural" as any other phase of life—as natural as childbirth, for example. A particular dying person may be suffering physical or mental anguish, but the dying process itself is not automatically equivalent to personal pathology, even though it may be accompanied by somatic illness and deterioration.

2. As an extension of the preceding point, the authors suggest that there is a preterminal period that may be regarded as a developmental phase. This has been generally ignored by psychiatrists and developmental psychologists. Specific characteristics of the preterminal developmental phase can be described with reasonable accuracy when we begin to observe systematically all aspects of the dying person, not only his medical symptoms and vital signs.

3. Extreme care must therefore be taken to disentangle observations from implicit value judgments. One outstanding example will be cited. A few years ago relatively little attention was given to the psychosocial situation of elderly citizens. Currently, there is a strong upsurge of interest in the aged, taking form in legislation, research, and action programs. This has created a marked tendency to characterize aging, not as a process, but as a problem. Many essays and proposals on the subject of aging seem to assume that aging, per se, is a mental health problem. The same sequence is now possible with the subject of dying. Preceding from a viewpoint of neglect, we may now be moving toward a period of "discovery" of dying and then, almost imperceptibly, to the assumption that dying per se is just one more "mental health problem." The authors are not convinced that

the translation of every phase of human life into the terms of a "mental health problem" is in the best interests of our society or that it represents the most trenchant scientific approach. It should be made clear that although this study applies psychiatric and psychological procedures to the study of the dying process, this by no means implies that this process is considered a mental health problem.

4. Care of the dying may at times be assigned to specialists such as physicians and nurses and even to specific members of the family. Ultimately, however, responsibility for the dying person and his place in society belongs to the community as a whole. The values and customs of each community influence the way in which people die and the pattern of response within the group. The psychological autopsy is only one method whereby we can appraise the ways in which the community integrates or isolates the dying, accepts or sloughs off responsibility, hastens or delays the advent of death. Furthermore, what can the survivors learn from the dying that may be applied to their own lives? What information and skill can be acquired by those who will be called upon to care for the dying— those who must ultimately relate themselves to the dying? These are among the many relevant questions that the community should ask, and to which the psychological autopsy seeks to provide answers.

II THE INSTITUTIONAL SETTING

The observations reported here are based on the reconstruction of the terminal phase of life in 80 elderly men and women who were patients in Cushing Hospital, Framingham, Massachusetts, at the time of death. The psychological autopsy series is part of a larger research and training project concerned with the psychosocial aspects of dying and death in hospitalized geriatric patients; other phases of the project have been reported elsewhere (Kastenbaum, 1965, 1966a, 1966b, 1967).

Cushing Hospital is an accredited hospital devoted exclusively to the care of men and women over the age of 65. It has been operated as a geriatric facility by the Commonwealth of Massachusetts since 1957. The average census in recent years has been 640 patients, and the age of the hospital population has gradually increased to its present level, which is a mean age of 83 years.

All admissions are voluntary. Most of the patients are able to care for themselves to some degree, but others require intensive nursing care and are limited to a bed-and-chair existence. Mental status covers a broad range from those who are completely alert and competent to some patients who appear to be confused and disoriented at all times.

Medical, nursing, and dental services are supplemented by occupational therapy, physical therapy, recreational therapy, psychology, social service, and chaplains who represent the three major religions. The hospital has many aspects of a self-contained community. It operates its own food, laundry, recreational, fire, and police services, as well as a greenhouse. Nevertheless, Cushing Hospital pursues an active "open-door" policy, including a volunteer program, and encourages many levels of interchange with the surrounding communities.

III THE PSYCHOLOGICAL AUTOPSY METHOD

The psychological autopsy is an interdisciplinary conference that attempts to evaluate the preterminal and terminal phases of life for a recently deceased patient and to determine the role of psychosocial factors in his death. The sessions are held weekly, with 15 to 20 participants. The proceedings follow a semistructured format and are recorded for subsequent analysis.

Case Selection

Members of the project staff conduct a preliminary review of all deaths. The span of selection is usually a period of about 10 days, during which as few as one or two, or as many as seven or eight, patients may have died. Selection of a case for psychological autopsy is usually made five or six days before the conference. Occasionally the choice of a case is dictated by salient conditions or questions, such as particularly strong staff interest in the patient, unusual circumstances of death, the fact that the deceased has a surviving spouse in the hospital, and so forth. The number of cases in which a nonrandom selection is made because of salient conditions is equaled by the number of cases that appear superficially to offer "nothing unusual," "nothing interesting," or even "no information." Many of the most challenging and informative sessions have centered around cases that were selected precisely because they appeared superficially to be of minimal interest. Apart from the salient cases and their counterbalancing "dull" cases, selections are made on a random basis

Preparation for the Session

A member of the project staff prepares a detailed abstract of the deceased patient's history from information available in medical records and supplements this material with whatever additional material might be available in the files of the psychology department or from reports by "friendly visitors" through the volunteer service. A short summary of the basic information is prepared and made available to each participant. A sample information sheet is shown in Figure 1. It will be noted that this information sheet does not include material that is interpretative, speculative, or otherwise likely to exert a biasing effect upon participants.

The patient's name is distributed to department heads and physicians; the nursing service sends two or three of its members who have known the patient and provides a supplementary list of nursing personnel who also knew the patient but who cannot be spared from their ward duties. Members of the project staff then interview the personnel on this supplementary list as well as other people who might have contributions to make but who cannot attend the session itself. Sometimes other patients, as well as staff members, are interviewed.

5

THE SESSION

A typical session includes the participation of a group of staff members who attend on a regular basis. There are 8 or 10 of these "regulars"— members of the psychology department, project staff, and social service. Nursing personnel (including supervisors, instructors, RN's, LPN's, and attendants), occupational therapists, chaplain, and others bring the total to between 15 and 20 at each session. Attendance by members of the medical service is irregular. Often the sessions include one or two guests, such as professional or research personnel who are visiting from other facilities.

The project director (Robert Kastenbaum) and psychiatric consultant (Avery D. Weisman) preside at these meetings and attempt to provide an opportunity for spontaneous and spirited discussion, to pursue follow-up questions, and to correlate information. The project director is a clinical and research psychologist who specializes in gerontology. The consultant is a psychoanalytic psychiatrist with research interest in the problems of dying patients.

The conference begins with a brief introduction by the project director and then turns to a review of the patient's medical course. This medical review is provided by a staff physician, when one is present, or by the consultant if no staff physician is available. Other participants then add

FIGURE 1

BACKGROUND INFORMATION SHEET (Sample)

Patient: Amy Wilton	Hospital No.: 0000	Age: 84

Personal History

Date of birth: March 18, 1882   Place of birth: Boston, Mass.
Parents' background: Both parents born in Boston
Marital status: Widowed
Children: 2 daughters, both living; one son died at age 49
Siblings: Oldest of 7 children. Survived by 4 sisters and 1 brother
Religion: Protestant   Occupation: Bakery worker; housewife
Past hospitalizations: Kearney Hospital, 1955, Diabetes Mellitus
                    Santa Rosa Hospital, 1957, Varicose veins

Cushing Hospital Stay

Admission date: 7-10-64   Length of stay: 21 months, 5 days
Admission diagnosis:
   1. Arteriosclerotic heart disease with aortic stenosis, compensated
   2. Diabetic Mellitus, controlled with insulin
      Diabetic retinopathy
      Hypothyroidism (history)
      Varicose veins of legs, bilateral

Ward Assignments: Ward	Length of Stay	Reason for Transfer
407	3 months	
305	17½ months	Administrative
406	3 weeks	More nursing care

Date of death: 4-14-66   Autopsy: performed
Cause of death: Cerebral thrombosis, due to cerebral arteriosclerosis. Other significant conditions: Diabetes Mellitus

their own information, which ranges from detailed written notes to inter-personal observations not previously recorded. The participants freely report their observations and interpretations; this presents a more complete picture of the deceased patient than any one staff member or department could have developed alone. The discussion that follows these reports is a co-operative attempt to raise questions and propose plausible hypotheses.

Since most hospital personnel (e.g., nurses, occupational therapists) do not regularly record behavioral changes or conversations with patients, their spontaneous recollections and seemingly random observations are frequently more informative than are the hospital charts. Similarly, during the open discussion, an untrained volunteer may contribute illuminating details or insights—information that otherwise would be lost. Many of the contributions are admittedly sketchy, inconsistent, and biased, but all have some relevance to the task of consolidating heterogeneous material into a simplified account of what really happened.

Not every resident of Cushing Hospital is a "sick" person in the usual sense of the word. Some patients are active, energetic, totally engaged participants in the various programs and facilities offered by the institution. Because of inclination or incapacity, other patients tend to withdraw and become isolated, almost unknown members of the hospital community. However, most patients lie somewhere between these extremes. The amount of information available about them seems to parallel the extent of their social visibility. As a result, there may be many sources for abundant information and pertinent observations about some patients, while other, less visible patients, despite long residence in the hospital, are known only to a few custodial personnel.

Recording and Analysis

Each psychological autopsy session is tape recorded. A project staff member also takes notes during the session. Later, a running account is prepared by combining the recording and the notes. In addition, critical issues, contradictions, unanswered questions, and implications for follow-up action are briefly summarized, and certain aspects of the case are abstracted in quantitative form for subsequent analysis. These aspects range from such straightforward facts as the patient's age at death to rating of mental status, which requires additional steps of analysis and sometimes cannot be made with complete accuracy. A few of these quantitative aspects have been reported elsewhere (Kastenbaum, 1966c; Kastenbaum & Weisman, in press), and others are still being developed.

The psychiatric consultant independently prepares his own summary of the case, including his clinical interpretations. The director and the consultant then collaborate in evaluating the case, and implications for research and training are discussed with the relevant staff members.

IV THE SAMPLE

The material presented here is based on the first 80 cases in the psychological autopsy series (still in progress). There was an equal number of men and women, with a median age at death of 83, ranging from 68 to 100. The median length of stay at Cushing Hospital was 31.5 months, with a range of 1 to 105 months. Both ranges are virtually identical with the total ranges for age and duration of hospitalization for the hospital population in general. Further information is presented in Tables 1 and 2. Most of the female patients were widowed. Chronic brain syndrome, cardiovascular and arthritic disorders, pneumonia and other respiratory conditions, and kidney disease were the predominant conditions associated with death.

TABLE 1

AGE AT DEATH OF FIRST 80 PSYCHOLOGICAL AUTOPSY PATIENTS

Age at Death	Males		Females		Combined	
	f	%	f	%	f	%
90+	7	17.50	8	20.00	15	18.75
80–89	19	47.50	20	50.00	39	48.75
68–79	14	35.00	12	30.00	26	32.50
Totals	40	100	40	100	80	100
Range	68–100		79–96		68–100	
Median	82		84		83	

TABLE 2

LENGTH OF STAY AT CUSHING HOSPITAL

Length of Stay	Males		Females		Combined	
	f	%	f	%	f	%
Less than 1 year	11	27.50	10	25.00	21	26.25
Less than 3 years	11	27.50	11	27.50	22	27.50
Less than 5 years	9	22.50	10	25.00	19	23.75
Less than 7 years	6	15.00	5	12.50	11	13.75
7 years or more	3	7.50	4	10.00	7	8.75
Totals	40	100	40	100	80	100
Range (months)	1–105		1–99		1–105	
Median stay (months)	30		33		31.5	

V OUTLINE OF TOPICS EXPLORED

The terminal phase of life in a geriatric institution may be divided into four stages, each with its own special occurrences and critical problems. These are the (a) prehospital situation, (b) hospital course, (c) preterminal period, and (d) final illness.

How a patient undergoes the transition from one stage to the next may influence the way in which he ultimately confronts death. However, when attempting to reconstruct the terminal phase after the patient has died, the staff explores these stages in reverse order from original sequence. In addition to the following questions, which apply to every case, the participants almost always formulate other questions that are suggested by the specific case material presented.

1. Final illness
   a. What was the patient's terminal illness?
   b. Did this illness differ substantially from the admission diagnoses?
   c. Was the death expected or unexpected at this time? Was death sudden or gradual?
   d. Was autopsy permission granted?
2. Preterminal period
   a. What was the patient's mental status and level of consciousness prior to the terminal illness?
   b. What happened that drew attention to mental, physical, or social changes?
   c. Did the patient ever refer openly to death and dying or give other indications of going downhill?
   d. Other than direct declarations about death, were there unusual utterances or behavior that may have served as premonitions?
   e. What was the extent and nature of his relationship with other people during the preterminal period?
3. Hospital course
   a. What was the extent and nature of the patient's relationship with people (other patients, staff, relatives, visitors, etc.) during his overall hospital course?
   b. How was the patient regarded by those who were in contact with him?
   c. What personal problems or crises developed, and how were they met?
4. Prehospital situation
   a. What was the patient's medical condition and mental status at the time of admission?
   b. What were the medical, social, and personal circumstances that led to hospitalization?
   c. What was the patient's attitude toward his admission?

This set of questions constitutes only a bare outline of the topics that are explored in the psychological autopsy session. It is not uncommon for any one of these questions to generate more specific inquiries and lead to prolonged discussion.

VI AUTOPSY FINDINGS AND ILLUSTRATIVE CASES

FINAL ILLNESS

Anatomical Findings

Details of anatomical findings are primarily the concern of the pathologist, not the psychologist. It may be significant, however, that most of these patients died with complications of vascular disease. These included acute and chronic myocardial infarction, pulmonary embolism, multiple cerebral thromboses, and intracerebral hemorrhage. There were also three patients with carcinoma, one with dissecting aortic aneurysm, one with undiagnosed volvulus, and one patient with terminal uremia. One man had been admitted with a diagnosis of monocytic leukemia but died 18 months later of an acute myocardial infarction.

There were other somatic factors that probably contributed to the terminal illness. Although major illnesses, such as amputation of an extremity, fracture of the neck of the femur, and even abdominal surgery are compatible with recovery, several such postoperative patients declined rapidly afterward. Enforced bed rest in many instances tended to create intractable confusion and delirium. The final illness seems also to be hastened by isolating some patients from familiar sources of reality testing. Their death is often brought about with the additional stress of pneumonia or minor urinary infection.

In cases where post-mortem anatomical findings do not adequately explain a death, it is tempting to invoke a psychosocial explanation. However, such an inference often would be unjustified, because psychosocial components in illness do not constitute a diagnosis. Even conspicuously aberrant psychological and social changes require the collaboration of abnormal biochemical and physiological changes to produce death. Moreover, unknown physical factors may also contribute to a patient's death.

Case 1. For many years an 87-year-old man had vehemently refused surgical correction of enormous bilateral inguinal hernias. His mental status during hospitalization was one of confusion and delirium. In addition, he developed severe inguinal edema, phimosis, and urinary infection. As a result of the deteriorating physical situation, the surgeon was forced to operate. Despite his misgivings, the patient relented and accepted the operation. After surgery, the patient became increasingly confused and agitated. This condition was only partially relieved during subsequent weeks when he visited his daughter's home. Several months later, his urinary infection became more severe; he lapsed into coma, and died.

There is probably little direct connection between the patient's adamant refusal to be operated upon and his subsequent death. However, it is possible that a combination of psychological and somatic factors could have exercised indirect influence. Chronic delirium may be initiated by defective reality testing and damaging changes in the patient's self-image. The delirium, in turn, may be followed by dehydration, exhaustion, sleeplessness, refusal to accept food, and minor injuries and infections. The cumulative effect of these stresses can build up to the point where they produce a life-and-death crisis. Despite intensive medical and surgical care, and regardless of the specific method of treatment, the patient's psychobiological depletion may be irreversible.

Autopsy Permission

Consent to perform a post-mortem examination is more than a legal requirement. It is also a means of evaluating the relationship between the doctor, the patient, and the patient's family. As a rule, the most neglectful and disinterested families are the ones who refuse permission for an autopsy. Signs of their disinterest include infrequent visits, overlooked birthdays, and unreasonable complaints about the patient's care.

The usual reasons for consenting to post-mortem examination do not apply in a geriatric institution. Because there is seldom scientific curiosity about a baffling diagnostic or therapeutic problem, consent becomes a personal issue. Many disinterested families claim that the patient has "suffered enough," without being at all sure whether the patient did or did not suffer during the final illness. These rationalizations are transparent devices to relieve their guilt or to make amends for neglecting the patient. In other instances, a family may not be able to accept the reality of a parent's death, and may look upon autopsy as an operation to which their father or mother would not have consented. One woman agreed to allow post-mortem examination of her mother, with whom she had a good relationship, but refused in the case of her father, whom she had always despised.

PRETERMINAL PERIOD

Mental Status and Level of Consciousness

In a chronic hospital, basic information about a patient's long-term mental status is rarely available. Aside from an occasional note by nurses or staff physicians, little is known about the patient's day-by-day orientation, mood, or thought content. However, when the patient develops symptoms that seem to herald the terminal period, or any other serious illness, the staff intensifies its treatment, observations, and care. Reactions to medicine are carefully recorded, and progress is closely watched. Consequently, changes in the content and quality of communication are also noted, because the staff is alerted to disturbed orientation, disability in taking care of one's own needs, and mental confusion.

In many instances, particularly when the patient has entered the terminal period without previous intensive care, there are only fragmentary accounts of mental changes or disturbances in consciousness. The staff then examines the hospital chart and interviews people who knew the patient best. As a rule, the staff is able to determine whether or not higher intellectual functions were impaired, or whether gross changes in perception, orientation, self-awareness, and language function had occurred. Furthermore, because medical examination during terminal illness is usually very attentive, information about reflex activity and the ability to respond to various stimuli is also available.

Despite shortcomings in observing and reporting changes in mental status and level of consciousness, it has been possible to recognize four types of mental status in preterminal patients, each with its own distinctive qualities. These are (a) alertness, (b) fluctuating states, (c) partial impairment, and (d) inaccessibility.

Alertness. Patients in this category customarily responded appropriately to ordinary conversation and to changes in daily circumstances. Language, self-perception, and judgment were not significantly impaired. Some patients in this category appeared to be completely free from mental impairment; other patients had slight memory defects or other impairments but to so slight a degree that there was no appreciable interference with their ability to comprehend what was going on.

Fluctuating states. Some patients were periodically confused, disoriented, and agitated. Occasional aphasic disturbances and hallucinatory phenomena —even fleeting paranoid ideas—were reported. However, such changes were temporary, and the patients subsequently showed only traces of mental impairment. These patients were described by staff members as having "good days" and "bad days," or seemed to be either confused or well-oriented according to the kind of situation or to how they were approached, etc.

Partial impairment. Many patients were permanently impaired in some significant aspect of mental function. This impairment did not often interfere with ward adjustment, but they became confused more easily and required more assistance and supervision than did more alert and self-reliant patients.

Inaccessibility. Some patients suffered from gross defects in cerebral function. They were unable to leave the ward without close supervision, failed to respond to simple requests, and often were confined to a bed-and-chair existence. Their needs were usually met by one or two of the ward personnel who had learned to interpret the patient's incoherent utterances and nonverbal behavior; otherwise, the mental life of these patients was completely inaccessible. Patients who became stuporous for other reasons during the preterminal period were also inaccessible. Naturally, in the final stage of the terminal period, many more patients lapsed into stupor or coma and were inaccessible.

A recent analysis of the first 61 psychological autopsy cases suggests that "almost all the dying geriatric patients in this sample had retained some ability to observe and interpret their situation" (Kastenbaum, 1966c). Approximately half of the total sample was consistently alert until their death or final comatose state. Although the available information was neither as comprehensive nor as reliable as would be required to derive indisputable, or solid, conclusions, all the evidence tended to indicate that most of these geriatric patients retained a reasonably high level of mental functioning, at least on occasion. These findings certainly did not support the assumption that most aged patients have minimal mental contact and are unaware of their condition and surroundings during their final hours or days.

An independent clinical review of the first 80 psychological autopsy cases by the senior author confirmed his earlier impression that practically all patients were at least partially accessible at some time during their terminal illness. This indicates that the staff might be able to communicate with seemingly unresponsive and dying patients far more often than would have been thought. Despite obvious difficulties in achieving wholly normal communication, there is still an opportunity for some contact with dying geriatric patients through the use of their residual functions. The fact that almost all patients retained an accessible level of mental functioning also argues against treatment programs and ward environments that are designed to meet only physical needs.

Our exploration of all available recorded and unrecorded material pertaining to these patients indicates how little emphasis has been placed upon observation and reporting of mental status by medical and nursing personnel, despite their dedication to the general well-being of patients. Many records contain meticulous medical notes but scarcely a word about mental status or level of consciousness. Reports of disorientation or hallucination are seldom supported by evidence or description of these aberrations. Rarer still are notes giving direct quotes of what the patients say about themselves. All too frequently, the psychological autopsy elicits only cursory observations about the personality and mental functioning of a dying patient. This meager supply of information could scarcely have been very useful in comprehensive treatment of the patient while he was still alive and seldom provides enough retrospective material to permit an evaluation of the relative proportion of biological, ethnic, personality, and mental status factors in the patient's entire pattern of decline. In some instances—and this is true of general hospitals as well—the dying patient is seemingly dehumanized; his final period of life is replaced by an account of agonal treatments.

Precipitating Events

What are the indications of a turn for the worse? The preterminal period is often heralded by an unequivocal medical, social, or mental event, and some of these precipitating events occur with almost dramatic force. Others are so inconspicuous that the staff recalls them only in retrospect. One day a patient may suddenly stop his habitual complaining and take to his bed, refuse to participate in his favorite activities, drastically reduce his food intake, and respond only in single words to every inquiry. After a few days or weeks of this unexplained regression, he may die just as mysteriously. Other patients fail to respond after a relatively minor operation or respiratory infection. Still others start the decline toward death after a particularly trying social crisis.

Case 2. An 85-year-old man had suffered with chronic bronchitis and emphysema for many years but was alert and active otherwise. He had eagerly anticipated going to his son's home for Thanksgiving, and when the day arrived he was dressed and ready, but no one came for him. He became more concerned as the hours went by. He asked the nurse about messages, but there were none, and he finally realized that he would spend the holiday at the hospital. After this disappointment, the patient kept more and more to himself, offered little, and accepted minimal care. Within a few weeks he was dead.

In reviewing the circumstances of death, the psychological autopsy discovered several other patients in whom a preterminal precipitant could have been recognized at its inception had the staff been alert to the possibility. However, most physicians and nurses are trained to respond to physical cues, not mental or social changes. A doctor, nurse, or aide frequently will either overlook a potentially significant event or will quickly reassure the patient, thus terminating the conversation.

Relevant psychosocial precipitants cannot be excluded even in cases where medical illness predominates. Burdened by the task of providing daily care, few doctors and nurses can spend enough time to acquaint themselves with the social and emotional context of every patient in whom minatory changes occur. Case 1 illustrates how a hernia operation precipitated confusion that persisted until death. Despite its surgical benefit, the emotional impact of an unwanted operation can scarcely be doubted.

Precipitants may be classified as *impersonal* (medical), *interpersonal* (social), or *intrapersonal* (mental) (Weisman & Hackett, 1961). However, most precipitating events are amalgams of all three of these dimensions and seldom are polarized enough to enable us to declare that one or another dimension predominates. Of course, if a patient is suddenly stricken with an extensive myocardial infarction while making enthusiastic plans for the future, this would usually be considered a somatic, or medical, precipitating event. On the other hand, if a patient quietly but firmly declares that it is time to die, withdraws from the group, refuses to communicate, and spurns even his food, this is probably a psychological precipitating event, even though the patient could not have died without the complicity of an aged body.

Medical Illness as a Precipitating Event

Case 3. An 80-year-old woman had always lived with her sister, who was five years older. Neither had ever married. When it was no longer possible to run the household and also care for her sister who had become progressively senile, hospital admission was sought by both sisters.

She adjusted well to the surroundings, enjoyed new acquaintances, maintained many former interests, and even developed into an artist of surprising skill. Her older sister, however, became steadily worse. Although the patient periodically complained of anginal pains and breathlessness, she did not refer to death. Three days before she suffered a fatal myocardial infarction, a distant cousin visited her. After the visit, she commented, "The doctors must think that I'm going to die!"

The only clues to serious illness in this patient were her dyspnea and chest pain, which were confirmed by electrocardiogram to be indicative of old myocardial damage. When a large infarction occurred, it was no surprise to the staff. Her comment after the cousin's visit was not accompanied by alarm, and no other significant psychosocial factors were apparent.

Social Crisis as a Precipitating Event

Case 4. An 84-year-old woman was admitted to the hospital six years after sustaining a right hemiparesis. Both the patient and her husband looked upon her stay as only a temporary placement. Their three children supported this idea and even regarded it lightly.

Although the patient seemed to get along well in the hospital, she wanted to go home. She had few visitors, despite her large family. As weeks became months and her children failed to cooperate in planning discharge with the social service department, it was apparent that the family had little intention of taking her home.

The patient did not directly complain about her predicament. On one occasion, however, while somewhat confused, she confided to a nurse that many years ago her husband had deserted her but voluntarily returned after an absence of five years.

Five months after she was admitted, her husband died suddenly of a heart attack. The family did not tell her about his death, nor did they want her to attend the funeral. Nevertheless, she seemed to have known about his death, because thereafter she spoke of him only in the past tense. Furthermore, her mental status deteriorated. Confusion was almost constant, and as she became more agitated and hallucinatory, she accused the nurses of neglecting her. At times she also argued with long-dead brothers and sisters. She hallucinated her father and complained to him about her husband's neglect and infidelity. Four months after her husband's death, she developed atrial fibrillation and died. The family, who had not visited her for several months, refused autopsy.

Although this patient had severe arteriosclerotic disease affecting brain and heart, she became much more confused after her husband's death. She seemed to know then that she would never return home. Concern about her husband's prolonged absence from home was reactivated during the final hallucinatory days. Neither husband nor children had helped her to accommodate to a permanent change. The children practically abandoned her after their father's death. Hence, abrupt accusations of neglect and infidelity directed toward the nursing staff and her husband seemed related to being neglected by her children. Evidently, the imagined presence of her dead father, brothers, and sisters enabled her to re-create and relive earlier, less forlorn days.

Hospitalized patients also may suffer disabling social crises that originate *within* the institution, as in the following case.

Case 5. During a long hospitalization, a 90-year-old widow had been indulgently, even affectionately, tolerated despite her imperious ways. For example, she was impatient with female personnel and even refused to allow a woman physician to examine her. She appreciated the attention of male attendants and developed a fairly close relationship with a young male social worker. She called him by his first name and enjoyed frequent conversations with him about her early life and about music and opera.

For unspecified administrative reasons, the patient was transferred to another ward where she was essentially unknown. Patients in the new ward were more deteriorated than she, but the head nurse presented the greatest difficulty. She was an elderly woman who called her charges "little girls," and, by assuming a patronizing attitude, fostered extreme dependency. The patient objected when the head nurse first called her by a diminutive version of her given name and demanded that she be called by her proper title. The nurse then sarcastically chided her for wanting to be the "Queen Bee!"

Three weeks later, a consultant found the patient in a state of delirium. She muttered servile pleas to go back to her original ward, reached out desperately to grab his hand and kiss it. By this time she had deteriorated so much that return to the former ward was no longer possible, and before other arrangements could be made, she died.

The staff had realized that this patient's only possessions were cultural interests, dignity, and memories of social status. Accordingly, they had accepted her angry outbursts with understanding and good humor. The antagonism between the patient and the head nurse did not come to light until the psychological autopsy. Then the staff learned how the patient had been infantilized and, in fact, persecuted for retaining relics of her earlier years.

Mental Changes as a Precipitating Event

Case 6. Five months before his death, a 75-year-old former stone mason first spoke about losing his will to live. Except for diminished vigor, nothing further was noted until he gave up his work in occupational therapy. Then, one morning, he asked for directions to a cemetery near his former home, stating that he was expecting the undertaker!

About a month before his death, he declared that his old employer had called and asked him to help dig graves for eight people. (In actuality, he had outlived seven siblings.) The delusion persisted, and every day he expected people to call for him and take him to the cemetery. Finally, he refused to leave his ward, lest he be away when they appeared. Two days before he died, he had several teeth extracted. He then asked if it was now time to call his sisters, about whom he had never spoken. He had no unusual physical complaints, and aside from his reluctance about leaving his ward, there were no changes in his institutional behavior. His death was attributed to cerebral thrombosis.

Case 7. Several weeks after celebrating his 100th birthday, the patient, an ex-farmer, became confused for the first time. Except for a prostatectomy when he was 80, he had never had a significant illness. He had worked until his hospital admission six years before, at the age of 94. After emptying a urinal near his bed without realizing what he was doing, the patient declared that he would rather die than deteriorate further. Thereafter, he refused food and drink and stayed in bed as long as possible each day. Although he was determined to end his life, his mental state was clearer at death than when the final illness had begun two weeks earlier.

Case 8. A 75-year-old married woman suffered from recurrent depressions for many years. She had been hospitalized many times and received most of the standard treatments for depression, with little improvement.

After she had been in the hospital for several months, her initial confusion and lethargy abated. Although remaining somewhat remote, she became a moderately well-adjusted, friendly member of the hospital community. Psychological testing disclosed severe organic impairment combined with preoccupation with themes of death, violence, and family turmoil. According to the examiner, she was in a chronic, constant rage, but no one had ever seen her angry. During visits by her family, she was usually silent and immobile. Her face was expressionless, even stony, as though too aggrieved even to register resentment. When speaking with members of the staff and other patients, she was cordial but reserved. She was proud of her grown family and their children. Her husband had retired several years earlier and, since her hospitalizations, spent much of his time in various resort cities. She spoke about him only with the utmost kindness and affection.

One weekend—perhaps because it was her 50th wedding anniversary—the patient abruptly put aside her habitual reserve and confessed to a friendly woman visitor that for many long years she had held back resentment toward her husband in order to preserve a façade of family harmony for her children. Her reticence gave way to bitter hatred as she denounced her husband for his cruelty, indifference, and flagrant affairs with other women. She was aware that, as repeated hospitalizations for depression occurred, her presence at home had not only become unnecessary but that she actually interfered with her family's way of life.

At the end of her tale, the patient was both exhausted and frightened, as indeed, was her visitor, who had not known how to interrupt. When the visitor returned the following day, the patient had resumed her usual benign and friendly manner. When another visitor asked her about her husband and their 50th anniversary, the patient explained that he was in Florida, and she would not want him to risk getting sick by coming home.

Then, with no further complaints, and without witnesses, she died the next day. No autopsy permission was obtained, and it was presumed that the cause of death was acute myocardial infarction.

These three cases demonstrate different ways in which predominantly mental changes seem to herald or to initiate death. In some respects, the patients in these three cases resemble patients who may be described as "predilected" to death (Weisman & Hackett, 1961). The first patient developed a delusion about returning to his former work but changed the locale to a cemetery. Although he did not mention his own death, he expected, and even anticipated, a man who would come soon to take him to the cemetery. His final illness had not caused prior symptoms, nor could cerebral arteriosclerosis in itself account for the patient's prolonged preparation for death.

After 100 years of exceedingly good health, the second patient preferred death to a life of progessive deterioration. While the first patient eagerly, but passively, awaited a "visit from the boss," the second man actively encouraged death. Neither man was suicidal. Their attitude was that it was time to die, despite the absence of serious illness. They differed only in the way they interpreted death.

The third patient had been seriously depressed for many years. Whether she had ever attempted suicide could not be ascertained. Perhaps it was only because of her 50th wedding anniversary that she allowed herself to pour out the indignation and hatred she had concealed for so long and to tell a friendly acquaintance about her loneliness and humiliation. How can her death be understood? She was undoubtedly exhausted and alarmed by her uncontrolled revelations to her visitor. After a night's sleep, she promptly returned to familiar rationalizations about her marriage. It is plausible that a combination of organic illness and the significant anniversary weekend had revived dormant conflicts, which then escaped repression and enabled her to disclose forbidden topics. Perhaps she had also sensed her imminent death and had reached out in a final effort to communicate with one of the few friendly people she knew.

Only the second patient spoke directly about death and seemed to seek it out. The delusion of the first patient and the dramatic disclosure of the third were complicated preludes to death, even though the time intervals differed. The actual process that links mental changes to fatal illness is an enigma, not a coincidence. In two of these patients, there was an "anniversary reaction," an event that is observed in both psychiatric patients and patients who face death from physical illness.

Premonitory Mental Symptoms

Observers who are alert to premonitions and predictions about death seek and find a host of clinical phenomena that may indicate impending death. However, conclusions drawn from these observations would be made less readily if it were further noted how often death does *not* follow. We have cited several instances of false declarations about death and have warned against misinterpreting banal statements in either direction unless quite complete information is available about the patient and his social context.

Although it is proper for the researcher to be skeptical about the number of patients who do anticipate their own death accurately, it is an unfortunate fact that patients are not usually allowed, even less encouraged, to express fears and beliefs about death. Even workers experienced in psychological interviewing find themselves avoiding dying patients or inadvertently terminating discussions about death. Furthermore, a recent study has indicated that nursing personnel most frequently terminate a patient's death-oriented comments with a distracting, denying, fatalistic, or reassuring remark. Exploration and discussion of the patient's mental state and his reason for introducing the subject are not often attempted (Kastenbaum, 1967). Death predictions and premonitions are unlikely to be expressed freely when the patient perceives that this topic is unwelcome.

How to recognize a "downhill" patient in advance is a challenging problem and must be dealt with quite apart from whether or not the patient directly talks about dying. If certain signs and symptoms of going downhill are recognized, an interested staff will intervene with appropriate therapy. But since there is no way to rerun such events, it is always possible that the beneficial effects of intervention is illusory.

*Case 9.** An 81-year-old childless widower was reported to have lost interest in his customary pastimes. He withdrew from conversations, ate sparingly, retired early, and tended to be confused. After a minor respiratory infection, he was thought to be "going downhill."

A psychiatric consultant learned that a short time before onset of these symptoms, the patient's favorite sister had died. She had lived nearby and had visited him regularly. Her children had not told their uncle that she was suffering from a serious illness. Consequently, she had been ill for several weeks when, suddenly, he learned of her death.

After discovering that the "downhill" symptoms had probably begun with grief and depression, the staff intervened to improve the situation. A volunteer worker befriended him, and other members of his large collateral family were encouraged to visit him frequently. They responded admirably. As a result, the patient rallied and resumed his customary activities. Six months later, he was continuing to make an excellent institutional adjustment.

Had the staff not learned about his sister's death, the patient might have been allowed to deteriorate further; it is even possible that the staff might never have known why. Depressed patients may too readily withdraw, and in the press of daily work no one finds out what initiates the change. Whether or not this patient would have passed into a terminal phase, of course, cannot be answered. However, had he died, the psychological autopsy might have concluded that the sister's death was a "social crisis as a precipitating event" for the patient's death. If this information had not been known, his death undoubtedly would have been ascribed to the relentless inroads of "natural causes." Fortunately, by seeking out sub-

---

* Cases 9, 10, and 20 are drawn from a separate study of patients who had been identified as possible preterminal risks. Some of these patients were studied in the psychological autopsy after the present series had been completed.

stitutes for his lost sister, the staff transformed a downhill course into a temporary setback.

Hallucinations and delusions. These are not uncommon among aged, institutionalized patients, but their content and adaptive purpose are often overlooked. Hallucinations and delusions are found, not only in patients with damaged brains, but also in patients with a damaged relation to reality. Institutional reality may appear bleak and impoverished, and disabilities of old age may enforce sensory and motor deprivation that can lead to still further social isolation.

Because aged patients with hallucinations and delusions have impaired reality testing, as well as a damaged reality to test, it is not surprising that they oppose so-called realistic evidence that contradicts their beliefs (Weisman, 1958). Nevertheless, the beliefs and perceptions that these patients retain often have a selective restorative significance in that they maintain relationships with people who are long dead, from whom they derived an optimal measure of emotional exchange (*e.g.,* Case 4).

Whether or not hallucinations and delusions are indicators of the onset of the preterminal period probably depends upon their content. It is more likely that hallucinations and delusions are primarily responses by a damaged brain to an impoverished world. When the margin between living and dying is obscure and the world is populated mainly by people who have already died, death and dying lose much of their threatening significance.

Case 10. An 87-year-old widow had been institutionalized for seven years because of progressive paralysis agitans and cerebrovascular disease. She was hostile and accusatory toward the staff. Her prolonged lapses of memory and seriously defective personal hygiene led to social isolation and impoverishment. In fact, she became almost forgotten, just as she herself forgot the meager events of her days.

A psychiatric consultant was surprised to find that, although the patient's memory for present events was grossly impaired, she could maintain an alert and intelligent conversation about the past, in which she confused her current life with past events and confabulated accordingly.

The patient described visits from her oldest brother, who, she said, was engaged in secret government work but who reported to her frequently about other members of the family. They also talked about earlier years, when both had shared their "big plans" for the future. She described how excited he had been when she was born, for she was the youngest child and only girl in a large family. He had always looked after her, and she had turned to him when she needed help.

When she was questioned further about her brother, she said that he "lived" in the cemetery, but this did not seem to her to be inconsistent with his visits, nor did she ever acknowledge that he was dead. On the other hand, when asked whether her husband ever visited her, she became bewildered. "Why, no . . . of course not . . . how could he? He's dead!"

Case 11. Four months before her death, an 89-year-old widow was admitted to the hospital. Although she had lived alone since the death of her last surviving child several months before, she could no longer continue to care for herself because of impaired vision, defective hearing, and general invalidism. She had no visitors, and her only remaining relatives were distant cousins.

The patient was widowed in her early thirties. She had supported her daughters while they were growing up by working as a housekeeper and governess. For many years she had managed a small vacation hotel where families returned with their children year after year. These friends had continued to remember her birthday each year, but she rarely saw them.

Two months after admission she fell, striking her head. No fracture was found, but she became more lethargic and confused and began to experience extremely detailed and vivid hallucinations. For example, she treated her head injury lightly and explained that she had become confused and had fallen because the children had been visiting her and had been running around the room. During the conversation, she spoke to her mother, who was presumably sitting next to her bed, and even called out to her old dog, Spot, who was out of sight at the foot of the bed.

Both of these aged women suffered from severe organic defects. They were isolated and, for a variety of reasons, were inaccessible to orientation visits by the staff. Consequently, they created their own circumscribed hallucinatory worlds, populated by well-remembered and dearly loved people with whom they had had a significant interchange. Remote recollections are often preserved by aged patients, although more recent information is lost. These patients did not distort daily events; retention was simply too severely impaired for them to respond even with delusions. Instead, they substituted gratifying recollections from the past to fill the gaps in recent memory.

Declarations about Death

Psychologists and social workers who conduct interviews at time of admission are convinced that most new patients fully expect to remain in the hospital until death. Yet explicit references to death were found in only about half of the psychological autopsy protocols, and a number of these references were so brief or vague that any evaluation of them was difficult. There are at least four explanations for this relatively small collection of explicit death references:

1. Institutionalized geriatric patients seldom think about death.

2. They think about death, but have no particular motivation for sharing their thoughts.

3. They think about death and wish to express their thoughts, but have nobody to listen to them.

4. They do speak about death, but their remarks either do not register upon the person to whom they were addressed or are soon forgotten.

Observations made both within the context of the psychological autopsy series and in related studies (Kastenbaum, 1965, 1967) suggest that explanations 3 and 4 are most significant. However, there is not sufficient information to draw definite conclusions about the relative influence of the alternative explanations. Nevertheless, there is the clear implication that explicit declarations about death (as recalled by staff members) probably represent only a fragmentary sampling of the patients' total orientations toward death.

From the available reports it appears that, in fact, only a few patients were able to predict their own death correctly. Others seemed to have a clear sense of its approach, and many expressed some intimation of death, without necessarily speaking about it in a straightforward manner. Nevertheless, premonitions or other statements about death constitute important clinical information, whether or not the statements ultimately prove to have been well-founded. These declarations often serve as an indication of the way in which the patient attempts to cope with a sense of crisis or loss. Ironically, talking about death, in itself, sometimes may alienate the very people upon whom the patient is calling for help.

Despair is often prompted by loss of physical capacity, of familiar surroundings, or loved ones. People who have lost all hope of complete restoration of capacity will also speak about death, dying, and even about already being dead. However, although investigators are inclined to recall a patient's vivid declarations about imminent death that actually came true, there are many equally unambiguous declarations about death that are not followed by death.

Case 12. An 80-year-old widow sent for the hospital chaplain to tell him that at 3 p.m. her blood was going to be drained away and that she would die! When the fateful time arrived and passed without mishap, she explained only that the operation had been postponed. Actually, no operation had been contemplated. She died four months later, without any further pronouncements about death.

Case 13. An 86-year-old widow died about nine months after admission. Although she was prepared to die at any time, and frequently spoke about the futility of her life, it was not until two months before death that she seemed to enter the preterminal period. At this time her only son was transferred to another part of the country. She then lost all interest in the hospital community, spoke briefly about joining her parents in the cemetery, withdrew entirely from ward activities, and spent most of her time reading the Bible. During the final two months of her life, she did not again refer to death.

Case 14. A 77-year-old woman had frequently felt herself to be near death after surgical operations and during periods of cardiac decompensation, yet she always managed to survive. During her hospital stay, she often predicted dire consequences for herself in order to induce various members of the staff to stay with her. Ironically, her actual death was unexpected and occurred during a period in which the patient was relatively symptom-free and in good spirits.

It is undoubtedly true that many geriatric patients speak about death from time to time without having their remarks heeded or recorded. Trite statements that incorporate ideas related to dying are common and frequently express merely dismay, pain, fright, or anger, so that few people expect every declaration about death to be a literal prophecy. Most patients become more taciturn in the preterminal period, instead of more outspoken. Even among aged patients who are preoccupied with death and may be statistically more vulnerable, there are many false prophecies. For these and other reasons, true declarations about death deserve special consideration. We may give little credence to banal statements about dying that are immediately followed by death, but the unexpected, vivid, or detailed declaration by a patient who has not previously been overtly preoccupied with death is of significance as an augury.

Case 15. During most of his three years in the hospital, a 76-year-old widower had been enthusiastic, alert, and convivial. Then, without known precipitant, he declared one day, "My time is almost here!" He began to fear being alone at night, lest he die unattended. Three days before his death, he consulted his lawyer and sold his house. An oversolicitous nurse refused to permit a psychologist to speak with him two days later, because he had been "too worried about death!" Death was attributed to chronic asthma and arteriosclerotic heart disease.

Case 16. A 77-year-old widow had not become reconciled to hospitalization until she returned from one of her frequent visits to her daughter's, where she had lived prior to admission. During this visit she discovered that all her possessions had been disposed of, including a pet dog.

It was noted that she was unusually optimistic on the day of her return and, when asked why, replied that she had a $2,000 insurance policy and that her tombstone was paid for. That same evening she refused an invitation to watch the movie and chose instead to read. First, however, she wheeled her TV set into another ward. Whether she had intended this as a gift could not be determined. Although she had had frequent anginal pains in the past, she did not complain of pain. She was found dead later in the evening.

Attitudes Toward Death

Even under favorable circumstances it is difficult to discover what any patient thinks or feels about death. In order to arrive at a judgment about preterminal attitudes toward death, the psychological autopsy is forced to rely upon sketchy observations, imperfect recollections, and tenuous inferences, reported by people with a limited psychological background. Direct declarations about death were recorded in only about half of the patients. In approximately half of the remaining group, even after extensive investigation, nothing at all could be learned about their attitude toward death. For the most part, direct information from the patients was sparse. It was significant that revealing quotes and observations often emerged only during the autopsy.

The staff described the patients' attitudes toward death as: (a) acceptance, (b) apathy, (c) apprehension, and (d) anticipation. Acceptance refers to patients who spoke about death in a dispassionate and realistic way; apathy describes patients who seemed indifferent to almost any event, including death; apprehension refers to patients who openly voiced fear and alarm about death; and anticipation applies to patients who showed acceptance plus an explicit wish for death.

Acceptance

Case 17. Until age and debility forced her to enter the hospital, a 90-year-old former teacher had been militantly independent. During her five-year hospital stay, she often spoke about death. She refused the chaplain's offer for prayer, declaring "I don't know anything about my birth—and I expect to know little about my death!" When a psychologist asked that she be tested, she said, "Do I need an I.Q. in order to die?" Her attitude was crisp, yet pleasant, alert, and responsive in every respect.

The patient accepted the inevitability of death and expected it in the foreseeable future. Her only wish—destined not to be fulfilled—was to die in her own home, so she could preserve the privacy she had always valued. She and her niece had already talked about funeral arrangements. The patient chose the people who were to be invited and requested that the casket lid be closed.

Despite realistic acceptance and modest wishes, her final days were difficult. She sustained an acute myocardial infarction and had to be transferred to the sick ward. The other patients were noisy, her bed was near the entrance, and her privacy was violated. As a result, her acceptance became almost a plea for death. "It is cruel to keep people alive when they want to die!" She dreamed that she had died and was about to be taken to a funeral home. On the day before her death, she told an old friend not to return, because she wanted him to remember her as she had been.

Apathy

Case 18. Shortly after the death of his wife, an 86-year-old childless widower was admitted to the hospital. His medical diagnoses were arteriosclerotic heart disease, osteoporosis, and hoarseness of undetermined origin. The latter symptom seemed to have dated from the time of his wife's death, but nothing further was learned about it, and, indeed, very little was ever learned about the patient.

Six months before death he fractured his hip. After this he became even less responsive. He refused food and never walked again, although he had no complaints and offered no explanation for his reluctance to be mobilized. He did not speak of his wife, even though her photograph was on the night stand. The staff did not realize that she had died just before he came to the hospital. In short, the patient was reasonable and cooperative but managed to shun any overtures toward establishing him as an active participant in the hospital community. It was evident that he had quietly resolved not to perpetuate his life.

Apprehension

Case 19. For about 10 years before admission, an 84-year-old widow had been in various nursing homes. She was convinced that the staff was under instructions to poison her and that she had been sent to the hospital to die. She fought with attendants, often screamed about death, and, for the most part, was grossly confused. During occasional clear periods, she would walk away from the hospital grounds. She declared herself to be 41 years old. This was when she had had a mastectomy for cancer—the event, perhaps, that mobilized fears of death. Nevertheless, despite fears of dying or being poisoned, the patient survived for two years and finally succumbed to terminal pneumonia. During the last weeks she moaned incessantly, crying out at times, "Where am I? Who am I?"

Anticipation

Case 20. An 84-year-old widow elected to leave the harmonious and affectionate atmosphere of the home her son had provided. After her husband's death, 25 years before, she had lived alone, but 12 years later, following a cataract operation, she was forced to give up her home and move in with her son and his family. The family was relatively affluent. She was evidently welcomed by all, and there were no restrictions because of space. The patient had many friends, and when diminished vision made outside visits with them impossible, she still spoke with them by telephone. She kept up her interests, which included books and hi-fi music. When she could no longer see to read, young people read to her, and she listened to recordings of famous books.

Two years before admission she fractured her hip during the first of several attacks of vertigo. As a result, she was confined to her room. Lest she become dizzy, or ill in some other way, the family insisted that someone be with her at all times. Gradually the patient became more aware of her invalidism and isolation. Many old friends had died or moved away, and telephone conversations with them were no longer possible; church attendance had become too difficult; nursing homes were not acceptable, because she regarded herself neither as incurably ill nor extremely aged, despite her advanced years and physical handicaps!

She was unusually alert, well-groomed, and looked no more than 70. She expressed herself exceedingly well as she described the events preceding admission and was thoroughly convincing as she reported that she was prepared to die. She never had been deeply despondent and regarded entry into the hospital as primarily a practical move. It was more appropriate to spend her final years in a hospital and to leave her son's home over his protest than to be merely tolerated there, should her care become more difficult. As the interview ended, she asked the consultant brightly, and almost as an afterthought, "Tell me, Doctor, will it be very long?" He had to ask what she meant. "I mean, will I live much longer?"

Acceptance was found more frequently than apprehension or alarm during the preterminal period (Kastenbaum, 1966c). Explicit fear of dying is relatively uncommon among aged patients, and seems to occur mainly in those who are highly disturbed and in those who show an advanced degree of organic deterioration. Less flamboyant expressions of anxiety or depression, however, may be overlooked. For example, one woman accepted without question the knowledge that an operation to remove an abdominal mass was necessary. The morning after she was told this, she reported dreaming that she had leaped from a "fright train" (sic) before a nameless calamity occurred. She did not recover consciousness following surgery.

Attitudes toward death are evaluated, not only on the basis of what patients say and do, but also by what they seem to feel. More subtle changes in affect or attitude are apt to escape notice, and relatively inconspicuous emotions may be neglected in favor of overt behavior and spoken sentiments. Depression without agitation was rare in these patients, as was anxiety about death. Since neither depression nor anxiety is an unusual emotion, the absence of both requires an explanation.

In addition to the likelihood that withdrawn and anxious patients often may not be noticed by the staff, the process of institutionalization and the duration of disability may serve to conceal depression and anxieties. In the course of extended institutionalization, emotional extremes become modulated, and affective expression itself is reduced. Periodically there will be outbursts of anger, panic, elation, or melancholia, but, for the most part, patients eventually achieve an accommodation to their status. Part of this accommodation includes acceptance of the reality of death, but the prolonged duration of disability itself may also tend to reduce overt emotional responses. In the early stages of serious illness many patients are alarmed and fearful lest they die. However, within a surprisingly short time, anxiety abates and is replaced by bland denial or remote concern. When they are in nursing homes, many patients learn that solitary endurance of discomfort, acceptance of the inevitable, and stoic compliance with impersonalized routine make for a more or less harmonious survival, tinged though it may be with alienation and despair. A similar situation may develop when an aged person's presence in the family home is unwelcome. Under these circumstances, death may seem to be the only logical release. Not infrequently, when patients who show depression and depletion are transferred to Cushing Hospital from nursing homes and other institutions, they seem to improve remarkably and at least part of their self-esteem becomes restored.

The question of the reality of a so-called will-to-live, or drive-to-survive, which can substantially influence a patient's prognosis, is a matter of conjecture. A recent study has indicated that physicians often do judge will-to-live to be a relevant variable in the survival potential of some geriatric patients (Kastenbaum, 1965). Nevertheless, there is no direct evidence concerning the validity of the will-to-live concept in the Cushing Hospital population. It is much easier to determine whether a patient accepts death as a personal fact or dreads it as an act akin to murder. Attitudes toward death, like declarations about death, vary with the patient's mood, mental status, and circumstances. Ideas revealed during intervals of good health may not be the same as those expressed during the terminal illness (Wolff, 1966). Acceptance and even anticipation of death, furthermore, should not be misinterpreted as indicating "denial" or "depression." Findings at Cushing Hospital suggest that acceptance is more often the attitude of reasonably well-adjusted patients, while death anxiety is often associated with moderately severe organic and psychiatric deterioration.

HOSPITAL COURSE

Understanding how patients get along in a geriatric institution is not the primary goal of the psychological autopsy. The reasons why some patients thrive and others deteriorate can be studied more effectively by other means. Discovering how patients maintain themselves as social beings throughout the hospital stay is of value primarily because it offers a standard of comparison for events of the terminal phase. Sometimes, however, in the press of daily hospital routine, some highly instructive situations may not be discovered until the psychological autopsy.

Case 21. After three years in the hospital, a 74-year-old man died of an acute cerebral hemorrhage. He had been regarded as one of the outstanding members of the hospital population because of his enthusiasm for new ventures, his helpful attitude toward other patients, and his unceasing appetite for learning.

The staff was surprised to discover, at the time of the psychological autopsy, that he had attended school only to the fourth grade and that he had been regarded as a harmless mental defective by his family. Aside from occasional maintenance work, he had had little contact with the world. For over 20 years he had made his home with a female cousin who was an invalid. When she became too feeble to be cared for at home, the family put her in a nursing home and sent the patient to Cushing Hospital, which they thought, erroneously, was an institution for defectives.

It was clear that the patient was at least normally intelligent and had an unusual capacity for inquiry. By seeking out the chaplain and the librarian, he pursued an active, albeit belated, program of self-education. He also learned to play the clarinet, drums, and harmonica and taught himself to paint, play billiards, and to bowl! On the day of his death, he had discussed buying a used clarinet.

This patient was a living refutation of the familiar aphorism that how people die is determined by how they have lived. Although most patients who enter a geriatric hospital expect to die and, in many cases, spend their remaining days in relative isolation and anonymity, the geriatric community is not necessarily a retreat where old people just sit around and wait for the clock to move relentlessly toward their hour of extinction. This man was truly untouched by the rewards, challenges, and disappointments that society insists upon. As a consequence, despite his age, he demonstrated that there was use for his untapped potential. He also demonstrated that it is not mandatory to accept the verdicts imposed by society.

PREHOSPITAL SITUATION

A patient's prehospital situation offers valuable information for the psychological autopsy, and its exploration is the task of a vigorous social service department. Only then can individualized programs be developed. Without thorough exploration of each patient's social background, care of the aged deteriorates into routine custody.

Patients at Cushing Hospital come from nursing homes, private or public hospitals, homes of their children or other members of the family, and, in some instances, from their own households. They include people who have lived affluently, as well as those who have required public assistance. Nevertheless, the vast majority is drawn from the so-called middle class, with occupations, education, values, and interests to match their economic status.

These social and personal characteristics sometimes make institutional adjustment more difficult than do medical diagnoses, which tend to be more uniform. The nursing staff and attendants, who are with the patients most of the time, are more apt to respond according to the expectations of their own social background than they are to the standards of their limited professional and occupational training. On a day-by-day basis, patients have relatively infrequent contact with physicians, psychologists, nursing supervisors, and social workers, who may be more flexible in their approach to different patients. For example, a former truck driver and stevedore was chided for his frequent use of profanity and sexual references. He was considered "obscene" and "promiscuous." However, investigation revealed that the patient's earthy conversation was in keeping with his background and that he was also highly respectful of professional staff members.

At the opposite extreme, patients who have had economic and educational advantages are often thought to be "snobs," or to "think themselves better" than those who take care of them. Consequently, patients are aware of an unspoken, yet incessant, pressure toward social conformity, which they must achieve both in act and in attitude. This means that mere obedience to hospital rules, demonstrated by standardized behavior, is not necessarily a sign of optimal adjustment. Compliance with institution-imposed values does not indicate a successful transition from the outside to the inside of the hospital. Patients who come from another institution seem to have less difficulty in adapting to the new one, even though they often have more severe physical illness and mental incapacity. Perhaps this is because patients who come from family households are forced (for the very first time) to deal with their established fears and prejudices about institutions and must also suffer the wrench of relinquishing their own homes. At first, the "fresh" group responds adversely to diminished alternatives and foresees only death.

The hospitalized group, in contrast, has already come to terms with institutional expectations. It has not yet been established, however, that there is a strong relationship between attitudes at time of hospital admission and length of survival. Factors involved in the differential longevity of patients from varied prehospital backgrounds are currently being studied.

VII DISCUSSION

THE PRETERMINAL PERIOD:
THEORETICAL AND PRACTICAL SIGNIFICANCE

Old people inevitably suffer repeated and depleting losses, simply as the price they must pay for outliving their contemporaries. Other losses and still more deprivation are brought about by steady constriction of social and emotional fields, by stagnation of human interchanges and rewards, and by increasing inability to cope with abrupt changes or to adjust to novelty. Diminished enthusiasm, rigidity of reality testing, and lack of adequate control over forthcoming events reduce still further the range of possible choices and the sense of harmonious accommodation to familiar circumstances.

In advanced age, inner infirmity and outer depletion may combine to make the margin between living and dying almost arbitrary. As Jules Henry (1963) says, our culture first glorifies death and destruction and then denies it, leaving our aged under an avalanche of obsolescence. Fortunately, these foreboding changes do not truly represent the aging process in general, nor are they found in every person who lives to an advanced age. However, we have often found similar changes during that phase of the closing years of life that we call the preterminal period. Further investigation of this period is of utmost relevance if we are to develop suitable methods of preserving rewarding participation by old people in the final phase of life.

The preterminal period may be defined as the transition point beyond which an aged person undergoes, not only the changes of senescence, but the incipient events of the final illness. Like other, more familiar transition stages, the preterminal period has no fixed time of onset, duration, or completion. Present information is scanty, and the preterminal period undoubtedly appears in many forms that have not yet been recognized. Our retrospective reconstruction of the final period of life has, however, clearly suggested that there is an observable period of physical and psychological accommodation to the imminence of death and that some patients are fully aware of these changes.

Because the medical observer usually looks for signs of recovery, or response to treatment, including that of drugs and operations, the indications of approaching death may be misinterpreted, minimized, or overlooked. Most often, the preterminal period is thought of as just a part of the final illness, instead of as an adaptive precursor to the terminal period.

Although indications of the preterminal period may be obscured by the immediacy of treating illness and by the aversion of the staff toward verbal and behavioral foreshadowing of death, it is almost impossible to walk through geriatric wards or talk with aged patients without realizing how deeply they are concerned with death. In some respects, their concern is more apparent than are various chronic symptoms. The positive signs of the preterminal period have been ignored largely because the aged themselves have been ignored. This is most apt to occur during the final years, when medical, social, and mental disabilities gradually merge into a final decline.

The preterminal period may not be limited to the time before death of aged patients in institutions. There may be analogous periods in other patients, afflicted with a variety of illnesses. The preterminal period of aged patients can be investigated more readily because these patients are rarely subjected to intensive treatment. As a result, there are fewer artifacts of illness or treatment to obscure observations.

Signs and Syndromes of the Preterminal Period

How can we recognize the preterminal period? We have only the sketchy and somewhat arbitrary observations of the psychological autopsy and the anecdotal evidence of individual cases to guide us. If there were established systems by which to recognize the reality of the preterminal period, our knowledge would be far more complete. At the present time, however, the most common signs are any changes that demonstrate diminished competence, control, perception, and performance. From a state of relatively good health, social, emotional, and physical adaptation shifts to "sickness unto death," accompanied by few signs of medical deterioration. Medical complications may be out of proportion to the degree of personality change. Although the preterminal period may be heralded by an acute medical emergency, other patients slip inconspicuously into the terminal phase. They may do less, speak less, complain less, and may even have to be urged to get out of bed, to eat, to wash, or to attend to bathroom needs. Talkative people fall silent; active people withdraw into semidormancy; and enthusiastic people become indifferent. To an outside observer, unable to converse with such patients, this appears as apathy, querulousness, senility, or simple dementia. These patients also seem less sensitive to pain and less responsive to environmental changes. They complain less, and because the attention of the staff is not drawn to them, these patients may therefore be more vulnerable to injuries, infections, and illnesses. Motivation may be reduced to the vanishing point. Memory defects become more pronounced, although some patients may, paradoxically, seem more acute during the terminal period. A variety of mental symptoms, such as hallucinations and delusions, serve as vivid substitutes for gaps in interaction with the contemporary world.

While the foregoing is perhaps the most common syndrome of the preterminal period, simple deterioration in performance, blunted emotional responses, and indifference to former interests do not, in themselves, demonstrate that there is a distinctive period worth studying. There are, however, other aged patients who indicate unmistakably that they have arrived at a critical juncture and who may even report premonitory awareness of death. Recognizing inner changes, these patients may then become reconciled to their disability and social disarticulation. They await the terminal period with acceptance and equanimity (Weisman & Hackett, 1961). Acceptance of death requires a degree of clarity and intact ego function; patients suffering from gross deterioration seem less able to adapt to the dying process.

Despite paucity of recorded observations, the medical and nursing staff will often recall, during the psychological autopsy, various unexpected comments and reversals in customary behavior demonstrated by the patients under discussion. In retrospect, these unanticipated changes were overtures to the final period. Thus, by wanting to protect their patients from direct confrontation with death, the staff may have precluded gaining valuable information and may possibly have allowed an opportunity for therapeutic intervention to slip by.

The preterminal period often seems to begin with a minor injury or trivial illness from which the patient fails to rally. But is the illness or injury a precipitant of the final illness or a result of a process that has already begun? The transition sometimes occurs after a patient openly acknowledges that return to an effective outside life is no longer feasible. It is less apparent in those patients who suffer a series of losses—real and implied—which bring about a cumulative despair. This despair may produce irreversible changes, both in social adjustment and personal accessibility. Many patients find death acceptable but not appropriate. Other patients find death appropriate, but still they cannot accept it, and linger on. How many people there are who yearn for death, but who cannot die, will probably never be determined. Yet among them are the people in whom despair and infirmity conspire, at a later date, to accelerate death.

Statements and predictions, by themselves, are unreliable signs of the preterminal period. More commonly, declarations about death are found among patients who have been forced to exchange familiar surroundings for a strange and uncongenial situation or who have undergone drastic revisions of their self-image. Newly admitted patients and those who are transferred from their ward to an unfamiliar part of the hospital can often protest only by inarticulately dying. We should not minimize the potential danger when an aged person's orientation or way of life is arbitrarily changed. For example, patients who have always valued independence and privacy are usually shocked by the uniformity and impersonality of a large medical ward. Although they may try to accommodate, the task may be too great for their waning capabilities. Ward rules and regulations, restricted choices or none at all about diet and sleeping arrangements, limited bathroom privileges and facilities, and even prohibitions about cherished possessions may be disturbing, even disastrous. It is exceedingly difficult for them to learn resignation, despite awareness of its necessity. Residual independence and token protest may appear in the guise of constant grumbling over trivia. Although some patients communicate only by complaining, among these are patients who are really disgusted at their own inability to die. In fact, when complaints cease and are followed by complete withdrawal, this may indicate that protest has become indifference; preferences, appetites, and the sense of being a separate person have finally been relinquished.

Preterminal syndromes undoubtedly appear in many other forms besides the familiar one of progressive apathy, detachment, querulousness, inertia, social invisibility, and lack of response to minor medical crises. Observers long ago learned that a patient who correctly, and without evidence of delusional or manipulative behavior, senses his imminent extinction may reveal an inner biological intelligence not available to objective testing. In a few instances, the staff has noted that the decline toward death begins after a key event, such as a birthday or anniversary. Although not always observed, these curious events may not be coincidences, because the "anniversary reaction" is a familiar one to psychiatrists.

In the medical literature of an earlier generation, the syndrome of "premortem clarity" was often reported (Munk, 1887). A moribund patient unexpectedly rallied, regained his faculties, and seemed on the verge of a remission. However, physicians learned that such episodes were deceptive. Instead of being an optimistic sign, premortem clarity and apparent remission signified that death could be expected soon, often within a day or two.

From our present viewpoint, we may wonder whether premortem clarity was another form of preterminal syndrome, because it was obviously not accompanied by concomitant improvement in the terminal disease. People who have observed patients during their final illness will often recall that, a few days before death, some patients roused from a deathbed stupor, ate with gusto, conversed with animation, complained but little, and even dressed themselves. Sometimes, physicians have been so misled by these actions that they have questioned their original diagnosis. It is just possible that these dramatic episodes are belated indications of a preterminal syndrome that began earlier. Once again, only systematic efforts to preserve communication and to evaluate mental status will answer this question. While the psychological autopsy is a valuable instrument with which to re-examine earlier observations, like the somatic autopsy, it cannot substitute for observations that were never made.

Preterminal Period as an Adaptational Phase

Throughout the life span there are familiar changes that occur so regularly that they have been called maturational or developmental phases. For the most part, these refer to the earlier phases of life, such as "infancy," "latency," "early school years," "adolescence," and so forth. The early years of life have been studied more exhaustively because physical growth and maturation are unmistakable during this time, even though subsidiary functions may be delayed.

According to a well-known theory of development (Erikson, 1966), there are successive levels of maturation, each with its special problems and crises. Adaptation at one level influences the way succeeding problems are resolved; failure during earlier periods will limit the types of resolution for problems that occur later. In general, the epigenetic theory holds that the capacity to manage successive adaptational crises is rooted in biological processes that are more or less uniform for the species. For example, a child learns to talk and walk only when his nervous system is ready, but, in itself, an intact nervous system does not guarantee successful walking and talking. In addition to the underlying biological preparation, the problems of development and the direction of development are influenced by the society in which a person must live. A child who is ready to walk and talk will learn the language of the people around him and will understand their expectations. One set of actions is approved, another is disapproved or punished, and, gradually, a child learns the prevailing values of his community. If he manages these successfully, he is presumed to pass on to the next developmental phase. When no special problems arise, this is called "adaptation." When problems arise and are not solved, the specific stage of development breaks down into separate "crises." The resulting crisis is then diagnosed according to the discipline that has the special vocabulary to describe it.

Because physical maturation is attained in the earlier phases of life, subsequent problems of adaptation are characterized less by biological processes than by cultural responses, group expectations, and symbolic directives. Hence, the overall concept of adaptational phases covers a wide range of events, from more or less uniform developmental changes, to culturally defined crises and rituals, to individualized episodes that are almost idiosyncratic within special groups. Their common purpose is to reduce tension between the organism and its world, even though, in some instances, the purpose seems to create the tension that it is then intended to reduce. These situations include quiescence of impulses, fulfillment of stereotyped modes of behavior, containment of threatening events, reconciliation with hostile objects, and, when necessary, their destruction. Adaptation may also require consolidation of purpose with those who are loved. In special circumstances, accommodation with prevailing values consistent with personal self-definition is also necessary. There is no single function or set of biological processes that can ensure "adaptation" as its unique outcome. The hypothesis of developmental phases only implies that at certain times there are outstanding problems that are geared both to social expectation and biological readiness. It does not mean that these problems occur only at such times, nor that they always can be resolved, once and for all. Perhaps the chief value of the hypothesis—as Selye (1956) has demonstrated in his discussion of biological processes—is as a method of investigation, not as a timetable of human events, nor as a set of objectives to measure oneself by.

The investigators' preliminary impression, gleaned from the study of aged people through the psychological autopsy, is that the preterminal period may be an adaptational phase, serving as a penultimate preparation for death. If so, then the signs and syndromes encountered are not just the symptoms of a disabled and disheartened person but are positive efforts of the organism to cope with residual problems from the past and to resolve the special crisis of the end of life. Its biological purpose, like that of earlier adaptational phases, is to reduce tension of a special kind; a keen awareness of life yields to serene acceptance of incipient death—a modulation that may hasten advent of the final illness.

When considering the possibility of an adaptational phase at the very end of life, we come face to face with many prejudices. Adaptation usually means growth and differentiation of personality to prepare for objectives yet to be achieved, not for extinction itself. Our society really has few concepts of a suitable role for its superannuated members (Blauner, 1966). Despite the inevitability of death, it is still regarded as an unmitigated calamity, except for the very old, who no longer serve a function. To some people, the idea that aged or dying people can achieve successful adaptation to the fact of imminent death, and may be helped in so doing, seems like sophistry or rationalization. How often has this opinion been tested out on the very aged or dying themselves? Would they agree that their final function is merely to cause survivors as little trouble as possible? We have socially approved methods for helping bereaved survivors, and even rituals for assisting those unaffected by death. There are few methods or rituals for the primary purpose of helping the dying person himself.

The concept of old age is closely associated with the idea of "maturity." If maturity is simply the end point of physical growth, it is reached in the early years of life, and at least two-thirds of our life expectancy is relegated to a kind of anticlimactic survival. If, however, maturity is measured by the capacity to fulfill cultural and social expectations, it is defined by all the norms and values of the middle years. We may ask, therefore, what kinds of values, expectations, and adaptations are feasible for people who are out of phase with these conventional concepts of maturity? Perhaps it is the very absence of well-defined expectations for the aged that has blinded observers to the occurrence of an adaptational phase late in life.

A stereotyped phantasy of youth is that the aged spend their remaining time reflecting upon past satisfactions and mistakes and reconciling themselves to inaction. Middle-aged people impose another stereotype and see the aged as older versions of themselves. Neither view is true, but neither is wholly false. There are societies in which the aged are said to be honored for their "wisdom," and because they transmit the traditions of the group from generation to generation. But these people are not superannuated; in no society are its senile or decrepit members honored simply for being ancient. The honored aged in more primitive societies are those whom we would call "mature," not senile.

The conclusion of the investigators, at this moment, is that the very old may be victims of their own value systems, because they continue to define themselves as residues. They have not learned that the terminal phase of life may be compatible with high-level and appropriate behavior (Weisman, 1966). Nowadays, when people reach retirement age they learn that retirement is not just a negative state of being unemployed. It can be a period of life full of special crises and problems that call forth previously unrecognized capacities and obligations. Perhaps, with a renewed study of the far end of life, we shall become more aware that the terminal period also has developmental, as well as adaptational, significance.

Mental Functioning in the Preterminal and Terminal Phases of Life

Alterations in mental life as people approach and enter the terminal phase of life have received only limited research attention. Although there has been little systematic investigation into any age group, the present study is focused entirely upon elderly patients. We do not need to belabor the point that optimal management of the dying patient's total situation requires an accurate and comprehensive understanding of his mental functioning. What is the developmental level of the dying person's thought processes? What are his primary and secondary thematic preoccupations? How is he orienting himself toward the prospect of impending death? Is there likely to be a relationship between changes in his mental life and the timing of his death? These are some of the questions that should be asked, both in research and clinical practice.

The purpose of this section is to review available research findings relevant to such questions, to consider the relationship between these questions and observations emerging from the psychological autopsy series, and to offer a few suggestions.

Scattered clinical observations have already suggested that changes in cognitive functioning might serve as predictors of death in the elderly, perhaps even before medical indications become obvious. Circumstantial support for this proposition was provided by a study of verbal learning in elderly psychiatric patients (Sanderson & Inglis, 1961). A sample of 15 geriatric patients with memory disorder was compared with an equal number of patients without memory disorder in a study involving the learning of new verbal material. As would be expected, the patients without memory disorder were more adept at new learning. When all the subjects were reviewed 16 months later, it was found that six members of the memory-disordered group had died, while all of the control group were living. Although the group studied was small, there was a statistically significant relationship between learning scores—a cognitive performance—and mortality. There was a closer relationship between memory disorder and mortality than between initial medical diagnosis and mortality.

A subsequent investigation by Lieberman and his colleagues (1965) tends to support and extend the Sanderson-Inglis results. Studying 30 volunteer subjects from a Jewish Orthodox home, Lieberman administered a battery of cognitive and personality measures at approximately monthly intervals for more than two years. Test performances of those who died and those who were still living at the end of this period were compared. It was found that the survivors showed relatively stable or even improving scores. However, those who died tended to manifest marked deterioration in performance during the 6- to 12-month period preceding death. Specifically, those who were soon to die tended to make simpler drawings of the human body and smaller or more disorganized reproductions of the Bender-Gestalt Test figures.

These findings reveal changes in the same person observed repeatedly over a period of time, whereas the Sanderson-Inglis results were limited to the relationship between a single baseline of functioning and the outcome variable of mortality. The fact that the two studies investigated entirely different groups of elderly people—psychiatric vs. nonpsychiatric—and used quite different measures of cognitive performance—verbal learning vs. free and reproduced drawings—suggests that the relationship between cognitive impairment and mortality might be a broad one. Clearly, however, these studies do not absolutely confirm, but only open the way to, the exploration of the cognition-mortality relationship.

Lieberman (1966) has continued his inquiry into the psychological correlates of impending death by analyzing data available from a longitudinal study of aged men and women who were in one of three different life situations: (a) waiting to enter an institution, (b) living in an institution, and

(c) living in the community without expecting to be institutionalized. Of greatest relevance here are the findings in the group of 22 subjects who died within a week to a year after completing a battery of wide-ranging tests and interviews.

The performance of the deceased subjects, as a group, did not differ from that of a matched group of survivors. However, when the deceased subjects were grouped according to their closeness to death at the time of testing, many differences emerged. There was lowered efficiency, diminished learning capacity, and reduced complexity of organization in the same degree as the subject's proximity to death. Those who were closer to death also showed heightened body preoccupation, lower expectation of gratification, and foreshortened future perspective.

Other preliminary results from this continuing investigation challenge conventional notions about the dying process: those who were near death tended to show heightened interest in people, heightened emotional reactivity, and low death preoccupation. Lieberman's work also suggests that psychological changes associated with the terminal phase of life form a pattern that can be differentiated empirically from the psychological changes associated with high vulnerability to stress.

Titchener and his colleagues investigated the psychological reactions to surgery of elderly men and women (1958). A total of 45 patients, all over age 65, were interviewed daily from admission until discharge. A relative or friend of each patient was also interviewed for background and corroborative material, and both the patient and his relative or friend were seen again for follow-up interviews three and six months after discharge.

Marked and progressive mental deterioration was found in 11 patients— about one-fourth of the group—following surgery. Among the etiologic factors, deterioration seemed to be more frequent in patients who had lost an accepting and comfortable home environment and, among the entire group, seemed most pronounced in the oldest patients. Depression, severe enough to be considered "disabling," was a common aftermath; 22 patients, or about one-half of the group, became depressed. The more severely depressed patients seemed to feel powerless to resist threat and stress. Nine patients developed paranoid ideas, usually "in response to real or imagined indifference of those persons significant to the elderly patient."

Titchener and his colleagues also found two different patterns of response to surgery, which they termed "renewal" and "depletion." Renewal was characterized by hope, freedom to continue activity, ability to invest in other objects, and so forth. Depletion was demonstrated by an awareness of personal deterioration, decreased ability to handle stress, and withdrawal of affect from external objects. Psychological depletion was regarded as predisposing patients to physical deterioration after surgery. While this study did not extend into the truly terminal phase of life, it does provide some clues to mental and emotional responses in a death-threat situation.

This handful of studies, along with the results of the psychological autopsy and other investigations being conducted by the authors, seems to make up the entire realm of direct psychological inquiry into the mental functioning of preterminal and terminal geriatric patients. Additional observations are sometimes picked up here and there, often as incidental findings in studies that have other purposes. Clinicians will occasionally report findings from informal studies. Although none of the available reports escapes methodological difficulties—the present study obviously included—it is clear that this topic is amenable to behavioral research and is perhaps no more difficult to pursue than are other aspects of complex human behavior.

More extensive research has been conducted into the death thoughts and attitudes of elderly people whose lives did not seem to be in particular jeopardy at the time of investigation. Munnichs (1966) has offered the most recent and detailed review of this literature. The methodological and semantic problems posed by these studies would require too lengthy discussion for the present purposes. Furthermore, there is an obvious limitation in all of the studies that diminishes their usefulness. Although it might be assumed that a number of the elderly subjects did expire relatively soon after being interviewed or tested, such protocols have not been identified or subjected to differential analysis. Therefore, it is not possible to separate potential death-premonition, death-prediction, or death-predilection cases from those with "normal" death thoughts and attitudes. Lack of follow-up investigation from a relatively healthy status through the terminal process limits the pertinence of these investigations.

With perhaps a middling sense of confidence, however, the investigators can offer a few tentative conclusions from the available research: (a) only a few elderly subjects express fear of death (Jeffers, Nichols, & Eisdorfer, 1961; Munnichs, op. cit.); (b) fear of death is more likely to be found among elderly people who are suffering from acute emotional or psychiatric disturbances (Christ, 1961); (c) elderly people manifest a variety of orienta tions toward death, not a uniform pattern (Feifel, 1956; Klopfer, 1947; Rhudick & Dibner, 1961; Wolff, 1966). Precise specification of these patterns and their correlates remains to be determined; in many areas, there are contradictions between the studies.

Observations made during the course of the psychological autopsy series tend to support the finding that there is a low incidence of death fear among elderly persons, especially those who seem close to their own death. These observations do not necessarily eliminate the possibility that death fear is *experienced* by many elderly people even though direct expressions are not often encountered or reported. Wolff, for example, believes that all elderly people fear death (1966). In a recent gerontological symposium, this topic was explored in greater detail (Kastenbaum, 1966d). In general, the material tends to confirm earlier observations of the higher incidence of manifest fear of death among psychiatrically disturbed patients, as well as the existence of a variety of death-orientation patterns (Bromberg & Schilder, 1933).

It is noteworthy that Lieberman found patterns of altered mental functioning—both positive and negative—preceding death in many of the elderly people he studied, while the authors' own observations suggest that most geriatric patients are in moderately good contact during the preterminal phase. Apparently, Lieberman's test battery is sensitive to changes in what might be termed the "formal dimensions" of mental functioning, which should be distinguished from what used to be known as "social intelligence." The authors' hunch is that geriatric patients may, indeed, undergo a number of changes in mental functioning, some adverse, during the months preceding death but that they continue to retain an adequate sense of what is happening to them within their total life situation. A longitudinal panel of studies, currently being undertaken as part of the whole project at Cushing Hospital, can be expected to contribute to this topic by combining some of the features of both the Lieberman and the psychological autopsy studies.

MANAGEMENT OF THE TERMINAL PHASE

Most people wonder from time to time what would happen if they had only a short time to live. Some think they might strive frantically to gather as much pleasure as possible in the time remaining. Others believe they would work harder, seeking to finish tasks planned for or already begun. Whatever their speculations, it is likely that most people would continue to live as they always have. Although they might reflect about the past and think about the never-to-be-realized future, few people, even when faced with a shortened and ever-shortening life expectancy, find it possible, expedient, or even desirable to change their habits and their ways of relating themselves to the world.

This is scarcely idle speculation among aged people. Actual life expectancy is relatively short, and any likelihood of substantially modifying their style of living is improbable. Indeed, their major concern is to preserve what is best and avoid the losses and penalties of being senescent.

In this section, ways to help the aged patient in an institutional setting are discussed. Although the larger problems of geriatric psychiatry (Berezin & Cath, 1965) and the management of terminal illness in general (Worcester, 1940) cannot wholly be put aside, specific findings are drawn upon to suggest ways that may make the transition from the preterminal period to exitus more acceptable and less distressing.

Successful management during the terminal phase requires that both the patient and the staff recognize and accept the possibility of hopeful, appropriate, and harmonious transition from a style of living to a style of dying (Weisman, 1966). The psychological autopsy has helped to formulate principles based upon psychological, medical, and sociological information. The investigators can therefore suggest ways to attain individualized treatment programs, coherent interdisciplinary procedures, and, in short, rational psychiatric management.

Psychiatric Management

When dealing with any patient who faces uncertain recovery or serious illness, it is sound medical practice to advise him about the overall situation. The patient is told about the diagnosis, the plan of treatment, and the probable course of his illness. Patients who know what to expect after an operation seem to require less pain medication (Egbert *et al.*, 1964). By having a sense of participation in their own treatment, patients develop fewer psychiatric complications (Hackett & Weisman, 1960). Unfortunately, these precautionary measures are often thought unnecessary when dealing with an aged patient. To be sure, a geriatric patient does not need to be told that he is growing older and can expect further infirmity. What often happens, however, is that when a patient reaches a specific age, usually about 65, many physicians thereafter tend to attribute all his symptoms to the erosions of time. Not only may serious and treatable illnesses be overlooked, but troublesome complaints are often regarded as trivial. Simply because he is growing older, a patient may be denied adequate medical care. As a result, psychiatric complications may proliferate.

A serious consequence of this fatalistic attitude is that the patient himself may become resigned to a state of hopeless infirmity. This, in itself, can be a pervasive sickness. Growing older is not a disease, but it may create sicknesses. Many aged people suffer from devaluation, not disease. Medical, social, and emotional forces may conspire to produce an *existential sickness*. Although convinced of their inevitable deterioration, many aged patients may still struggle to solve their problems but are prevented from doing so by the *definition* of senescence that our culture imposes upon them. Part of the difficulty is that the specific problems of aging are poorly defined. We have learned to expect specific problems in those who are growing up and we accept the discrepancies, irritations, vexations, paradoxes, and fearful conformities among adolescents. From one viewpoint, senescence is adolescence in reverse. The aged person is "growing down" to a more or less fixed position in which perception, performance, and communication seem to be, or actually are, impaired. Discrepancies, paradoxes, and irritations are only one phase of the many problems that geriatric psychiatry attempts to understand. In most instances, the problems of aging are not even formulated, let alone solved; so we must be appropriately tentative in proposing recommendations.

In the terminal phase, the rational psychiatric management of patients has five principal objectives: (a) adequate medical care, (b) encouragement of competent behavior, (c) preservation of rewarding relationships, (d) maintenance of a dignified self-image, and (e) attainment of an acceptable and, if possible, appropriate death.

Adequate Medical Care

To recommend adequate medical care may seem out of place in a discussion of psychiatric management. However, medical care includes, not only careful physical evaluation and medication for symptomatic care, but, above all, an attitude of caring (Homburger & Bonner, 1964). Psychiatric management does not mean that recommendations must be carried out by a psychiatrist. It is not too remote a possibility that psychologically adept practitioners, medical and nonmedical, will someday participate mutually in well-founded programs of comprehensive care.

Medication is practically always required in the terminal phase. This includes the period when patients are relatively well, not just during the final illness. Aged patients need care and medication for a host of complaints—insomnia, lack of appetite, constipation, fatigue, or nonspecific aches and pains. Not only do these complaints often register annoyance and discomfort in addition to whatever primary illness contributes to them, but they also reflect a wish to be taken seriously. Medication may be helpful physiologically, and the act of giving medication may indicate to a patient that he is being looked after in a highly personal way.

Because medical care thrives upon a satisfactory doctor-patient relationship, the medication itself may be less important than the manner in which it is given. After all, the cause of death of most aged patients in an institution is related to their admission diagnoses, not to new diseases. Most medications are intended to relieve symptoms and to reduce complaints; relatively few drugs are specific for individual diseases. When needed, most patients receive digitalis, antibiotics, colchicine, and so forth, because most physicians readily diagnose heart failure, infections, and gout. So-called minor complaints and refractory symptoms that have no visible anatomical foundation create the troublesome problem, however, and disrupt the doctor-patient relationship. If, for example, physicians or nurses seem to belittle minor symptoms, patients may respond as if they had been personally belittled. Lest they incur further rebukes, patients may then avoid staff members and not voice any complaints. We have learned, for instance, that some patients have spoken out, at least once, about death. Yet no details of what this signified were reported, and follow-up information was sadly lacking. We realize that a "good" patient is sometimes defined as one who causes no trouble, a fact that many patients realize, too. What does this indicate about comprehensive care? What happened to the patient who once reached out to someone in order to talk about dying? If medical care is limited to an occasional pill, administered only in response to the patient's pleas, it is easy to understand why so few patients are reported to be depressed or concerned about death. Silence, social invisibility, and conformity are not necessarily indications that a patient requires little care. Indeed, these may be symptoms of incipient depression or even the onset of the preterminal period.

This is not, of course, to suggest that elderly patients be overmedicated for captious complaints or to relieve institutional boredom. There are other therapeutic measures available for these symptoms. But physicians, nurses, and aides are reminded that although medication may restore functional impairments, medical and nursing *care* helps to restore and support diminished and damaged relationships. Having to ask repeatedly for some token of care—and this may be medication—is like begging to be cared for or asking for a gift; the request neutralizes the benefit. In terminal illness many patients wait too long before asking for medication; habits formed long before the final illness prevent these patients from openly acknowledging their need and expecting a response.

Alliance with a staff physician, nurse, aide, or ancillary worker may be therapeutic in itself. Aged, institutionalized patients depend upon continuity of care. This includes continuity of familiar faces who are accustomed to their idiosyncrasies and requirements. Old people often stake out a territorial claim in some corner of their home ward and dread displacement from it. They dislike personnel replacements and shifts from one ward to another, especially when these changes seem arbitrary or tend to imply indifference.

Encouragement of Competent Behavior

Medical treatment of physical disability may promote survival, but it is not enough to ensure *significant* survival. Ways to sustain competent and responsible behavior may be found by first establishing consistent and supportive physical circumstances, then by preserving optimal communication, and finally by providing tasks within the limits of competence and upon as high a level of achievement as possible.

Hope is contingent upon competence, not mere viability. For many people, incapacity is more agonizing than the prospect of death. The realities of having motivated tasks to accomplish and being able to communicate adequately are the preconditions of competent behavior. Sometimes it is assumed that only patients with obvious disturbances in understanding and expressing language require speech therapy. This is as erroneous as believing that occupational therapy is only a form of recreation. Both speech therapy and occupational therapy are effective avenues in sustaining and training methods of renewed communication and competence. They are useful for any patient whose impaired communication and loss of competence are significant threats. As a rule, patients who have been skilled workmen will refuse to continue their occupation as a diversion or hobby; they are too intolerant of their diminished abilities. Participation in an entirely new area is often encouraged, not only because it requires essentially untapped potential, but because such patients do not hold themselves up to as high standards of performance and therefore do not become so easily discouraged.

The mutual interdependence of communication and competent behavior is particularly apparent in patients who show unmistakable deterioration of mental status, language function, and motor skill (Talland, 1966). Multiple cerebral thrombosis may first be suspected, long before gross skeletal weaknesses appear, by a patient's poor retention of new learning material. Patients may be able to read, write, and speak without obvious agnosias and aphasias. But if they are not able to read with appreciation, to write coherent sentences, or to speak intelligibly, their level of competence and communication is so drastically reduced that their sense of responsibility and worth may be affected.

The psychological autopsy has often found that some terminal problems might have been avoided if more concerted efforts to preserve communication had been maintained. Few patients are wholly inaccessible, despite severe organic disturbances. Because an aged patient is disoriented, does not readily respond when asked about the date, and seems to know little about the current world situation, we should not conclude that he has lost all capacity to respond to familiar sights and sounds or that he cannot still react to reminders of past realities. One man, for example, was aphasic as well as paralyzed. He could not speak, even to convey his basic needs. Yet when his native land was mentioned, he wept. We can only speculate about how he might have responded if someone could have spoken to him in his native language.

The most effective way to maintain communication is to anticipate impairment and to establish auxiliary methods for transmitting messages. Patients with visual difficulties, for example, can be encouraged to make greater use of auditory cues, particularly by means of reasonable conversation. It is difficult to initiate conversation with some aged patients who have impaired memory for current dates and recent events; these patients often believe their mental status is being tested, and they respond with seemingly unreasonable anger. This problem may be partially prevented by offering orienting information when making other kinds of inquiries. We have found that even an elementary act of common courtesy, such as being addressed by name and title, will evoke a favorable response. Many patients have intact reality testing that seems impaired only when the staff demands an immediate response. Because so-called rigidity prevents some patients from quick adjustment to changes in conversation, they may be diagnosed as showing "perseveration." By failing to react rapidly and precisely to environmental changes, aged patients are often thought "confused." Accordingly, such patients may sense this and, accepting changes in how they are treated, may then act the way the diagnosis of "confusion" demands.

Many lonely and isolated people are both consoled and oriented by television and radio. Even patients with organic deterioration seem to benefit from having this common field of experience with others. Although the disembodied sights and sounds of public communication lack the individuality of personal contact, reality testing is preserved in a more continuous way through these media than by having nothing to relate to but hospital routine. As much as possible, responsible and diversified connections with the world must be maintained. Reality testing cannot be held at a competent level without a rational reality to test.

Preservation of Rewarding Relationships

The mutual exchange of human responses is a strong factor in preserving reality testing. This becomes even more significant when the exchange is between the patient and his family and friends. Visits from the "outside" may be highly desirable for many patients, while contact with inappropriately concerned, depressed, or excessively dutiful members of the family may distress other patients. It was discovered during the autopsy sessions that some patients seemed to enter the preterminal period shortly after a weekend visit to the home of a daughter or son. The staff presumed that the patient recognized that many changes had occurred and that their absence was no longer even noticed. However, this may be an unfair presumption, and until reliable information about the family and patient in the prehospital situation can be obtained, we can only speculate. One of the most important functions of the social worker in a geriatric institution is to form a candid relationship with the family. This helps, not only to establish baseline knowledge of the patient's behavior, but to provide information that can be used in planning treatment programs. Some families, for example, when applying for a patient's admission, will stress only the positive side of their relationship and, knowingly or not, will conceal the problems encountered in trying to provide a home for their aged parent. It is usually more important to know what kind of problems they had than whether the relationship was good or bad. Candid discussion with family members may encourage them to visit more often and even more effectively. Families may visit an aged relative only as an ordeal, sometimes even as a "death watch," because they know the patient has only a limited time to live. Less frequent visits, therefore, might be more appreciated by everyone concerned. Tactful reassurance that their visits are not obligatory could well improve the quality of the relationship as a whole. Some visitors are unnaturally optimistic and make gratuitous comments and promises that cannot be fulfilled. Others cannot speak freely with a patient but disguise this by truculent concern about trivia and fancied neglect. When relatives stir up the staff with complaints that often can be traced to the family's own shortcomings, they only increase the distance between the patient and the staff and often between the patient and his family.

Visits from younger people are often helpful, especially when they express interest in the patient's earlier experiences. In contrast, sons and daughters may have nothing more to say to their aged parent. Bored and depleted by the relationship, they, too, become part of the interminable routine. At first, older people may find it difficult to accept visits from strangers, even friendly visitors. Later on, these conversations may be eagerly anticipated, perhaps because the new acquaintances have a higher tolerance for their foibles and ancient anecdotes.

Maintenance of a Dignified Self-Image

One of the results of competent behavior and rewarding relationships is improvement in the patient's perception of his own worth. Ironically, the sense of self-esteem is frequently an early victim of the institutional process. In the course of tending to a busy hospital ward, even the most dedicated nurses and attendants must emphasize the simple physical requirements of large numbers of patients. Heeding the physical needs of the many has priority over attending to individual complaints, repetitious demands, and arbitrary claims upon the aides' time. Inevitably, in some cases patient care must be reduced to the lowest common denominator of practicality. Beds may be too close to each other; incompatible people may be forced to spend months side by side; lifetime habits of bathing, sleeping, or eating may be altered overnight. Even the sense of having privacy and personal possessions may be violated without a word of explanation or regret. In short, by using the excuse of "practicality," the process of institutionalization can convert all remnants of individuality into an encumbrance.

The investigators maintain that institutional efficiency could well be increased if closer attention were paid to factors that help to preserve a patient's favorable self-esteem. Mental status and performance will be improved, and the necessary steps to this end are surprisingly simple and wholly consistent with a well-run institution.

Among many other factors, the self-image is influenced by attention to privacy, possessions, respect for individuality, and self-esteem. Each of these can be assured the patient with a minimum of additional effort by the staff. Actually, the rewards of such efforts may even lessen the total burden of work in the long run.

Privacy, personal possessions, respect for individuality, and self-esteem are simply different phases of a relationship between staff and patient, especially when both are institutionalized. But there are differences between these factors, and one does not follow from the other. For example, although calling an older person by his first name may sometimes express an informal friendliness of spirit, more often it divests him of respect. It is preferable that aged patients be called by their proper title, but it is even more important that they be called *something*, not merely alluded to as an anonymous object. Part of the pejorative aspect of institutionalization is that people become impersonalized and that there is less and less difference between patient and staff. Conscientious respect for patients, even, or especially, those who are regressed, psychotic, or incompetent, may increase the staff's sense of worth in what they are doing, as well as help the patient. Of course, most attendants and aides might vigorously deny any disrespect for their charges. Yet in the course of their daily duties, they do not hesitate to enter rooms without knocking, pull back bedclothes without consideration for modesty, address patients with impersonal orders, and transfer them from one ward to another without a word of explanation.

The problem of personal possessions requires considerable tact and discretion. Many aged patients retain a few objects and mementos to remind them of a tangible past. To an outsider, many of the traits and habits of aged patients seem very peculiar. For example, some patients insist upon keeping old greeting cards, reading and rereading them long after the holiday has passed. Other patients keep notebooks in which they make almost indecipherable entries but which are personally significant to them. One man had at least a dozen small datebooks in which he recorded birthdays, anniversaries, deaths of friends, and famous events. From the attendants' viewpoint, possessions like this are "junk," which, in all fairness, does consume space and collect dust. Instead of arbitrarily taking away every scrap of personal life, however carefully it may be stored, it is probably more desirable to reach a compromise with each patient about which items are truly keepsakes and which are only clutter.

Attainment of an Acceptable Death

Much of the preceding pertains to the care of geriatric patients in general, not just the terminal patient. However, everything that is done during the hospital course finally reaches an end point. After all, each policy and intervention should have as one of its goals the achievement of a situation in which death is an acceptable fact of life (Choron, 1964). Death may be interpreted as a defeat by some members of the staff, who foresee that all of their ministrations are doomed; this attitude is the generally accepted philosophy of the health professions. However, it is not necessarily one that patients would share, nor is it the best philosophy to follow as a guiding principle. Death is not always a sign of defeat, error, or fallibility. The work at Cushing Hospital indicates that the terminal period usually finds patients ready to accept death, even prepared to welcome it. Apprehension about dying, on the other hand, is a symptom usually found among people who are relatively healthy and is, as a rule, an indication of inner conflict, not a realistic appraisal of actual, imminent danger. Weisman and Hackett (1962) found that most patients dying of cancer become reconciled to death and ask only that painful symptoms be controlled. Consequently, intelligent interventions by the staff can be of enormous assistance during the terminal period.

At any time during hospitalization, patients need an opportunity to talk about themselves. This becomes particularly urgent during the terminal period, when a patient's capacity to choose, to control, and to be conscious of a variety of events is greatly diminished.

The investigators believe that by preserving a patient's self-esteem and by respecting his individuality as long as possible he can face death with the same dignity that he had during life. Ideally, of course, we would want death to be not only acceptable but appropriate (Weisman, 1966; Weisman & Hackett, 1961). The concept of an appropriate death is based upon the view that dying can be a positive act, not just a calamity that overtakes a person. In appropriate death, the patient is helped to resolve conflict within the limits of his personality and in accordance with the aspirations of his ego ideal. Admittedly, an appropriate death is usually only partially attained, but it is a feasible goal to work toward. An appropriate death is, essentially, one that the patient might have chosen for himself, had he a choice. Conversely, whatever is done to impoverish, demean, or reduce a patient's autonomy and self-esteem will necessarily be a defeat for those who look after him.

Types of Psychiatric Intervention

Specific rules cannot be given for psychiatric interventions—and should not be. Treatment is always an individualized program, depending not only upon the patient but upon the ingenuity of the therapist, the dedication of the staff, and the circumstances within the institution. In this section, different *types* of psychiatric intervention are described. By no means should these types be confused with distinct methods of psychotherapy. Psychiatric interventions combine many elements of therapy drawn from other kinds of interactions with patients. They do not depend exclusively upon words and can be regarded as the guiding principles behind many procedures. Some interventions are intuitive improvisations; others are specifically planned.

The prerequisite of successful intervention is competent medical and nursing care, as well as conscientious attendance by every member of the professional and nonprofessional staff. During the terminal period, however, interventions demand special training to bring about the most beneficial attitude and use of skill. While the individual requirements of patients may be answered by spontaneous responses and intuitive inferences, being willing to help is, unfortunately, not the same as being able to help or knowing what to do. An effective program requires an ability to observe changes as well as to carry out procedures. What is observed and how it is observed are parts of treatment. Each intervention brings about fresh observations, and these, in turn, lead to further refinements of existing programs.

A psychiatric intervention may be defined as a systematic combination of what one does or says in order to effect a specific change in a patient's attitude or behavior. As noted earlier, psychiatric interventions are not restricted to professional psychiatrists. Anyone who is in a therapeutic relationship to a patient is thereby a therapist. Similarly, psychiatric interventions are wholly within the scope of anyone who makes himself accessible to patients.

The five objectives of psychiatric management are, to repeat, adequate medical care, encouragement of competent behavior, preservation of rewarding relationships, maintenance of a dignified self-image, and attainment of an acceptable death. There are three general types of intervention, intended to strengthen the sense of reality, to preserve reality testing, and to facilitate better ways of coping with events in the terminal stage. The investigators have named these interventions according to the particular aspect of reality they want to support and have called them evocative, informative, and substantive interventions.

Evocative interventions. This type of intervention is primarily aimed at eliciting appropriate emotional responses and modulating emotional extremes. Is the patient apprehensive or alarmed? Is he silent because of depression, or is he just resigned to a quiet end? Is he angry, apathetic, bitter, confused, compliant? Why is he concerned with trivia? Why is he so argumentative about irrelevant matters?

Exaggerated or unusual emotional responses during the terminal period may indicate that a patient's sense of reality for the world or his sense of individuality for himself has been damaged. If so, he may need help from an authentic representative of reality. Doctors and nurses usually do more than order medication and carry out procedures. Ward aides, too, mean more to patients than their jobs imply. All staff personnel should be aware of how important their presence may be, and they should be able to respond selectively to patients in order to counteract the isolation of sickness and the disarticulation of dying alone. Just the presence of someone who responds honestly, speaks a few words that truly reflect a sense of caring, or even remains intelligently silent may help to preserve a patient's attachment to the world. Careful listening is an art that is not easily acquired, because few people can tolerate being in the presence of conflict, let alone the imminence of death, without feeling impelled to speak. These comments, well-intended to be sure, may be inappropriate. Often such statements are meant to relieve the tension and anguish of the healthy person who stands by, not to help the patient. It is the presence of a true ally that really counts, not the repeated examination, another consultation, or still another medication. The confident presence of another may make it *unnecessary* for the patient to become confused.

Informative interventions. As the term implies, this type of intervention depends upon the mutual exchange of information between patient and therapist. Aged people may suffer from impaired reality testing, especially during the terminal period. In order to forestall confusion or hallucinatory regression, it is frequently necessary to offer orienting information, to check on the use of language, and to correct erroneous interpretations of surrounding events. As a preventive measure, patients need more information about themselves, their illness, and the environment in which they live, so they can fortify waning controls and self-regulatory abilities.

When primary perceptual organs are impaired, or when outside information is ambiguous, sketchy, or grossly reduced, hospitalized patients in the terminal phase may experience impairment of primary reality testing. When patients have a damaged nervous system and cannot properly integrate information, communicate ideas, or register anything beyond the most elementary wishes, they have defective secondary reality testing. Even with adequate information coming in from the outside, these patients cannot properly understand, articulate, or connect information in response to the demands of the world around them. Consequently, they may revert to a more primitive reality testing and restore an earlier version of reality. To observers, they seem to withdraw, to be confused, to be deluded, and to hallucinate.

Interventions that offer orienting or corrective information should not be confused with psychotherapeutic "interpretations." Although patients may sometimes be helped by knowing *why* they act in erratic ways, patients of advanced age are more often helped by knowing *that* they have acted inappropriately and that something can be done about it. Careful explanation and unambiguous guidance are excellent ways to counter the confusion of any unusual event. Criticism and intolerance for a patient's hesitant protests only aggravate faltering capacities to test reality. For example, if a patient knows why it is necessary to transfer him from a familiar ward, or to have a minor, but puzzling, laboratory test, he might be less inclined to be confused, depressed, or paranoid. He might also feel less like an administrative burden or simply a nonentity were he given enough information to permit him to respond more suitably to the proposed change. Repeatedly, the investigators observed during the autopsies that the neediest patients, from a psychological viewpoint, were those who were permitted to become "invisible." Few notes were written about their "progress." Nothing was done to reverse their downward course of alienation and withdrawal, and they were given very little information about themselves. When no information is sought or offered, none can be exchanged.

Unless a patient is given adequate and appropriate information about what is going on, ordinary channels of perception, communication, and performance are closed to him. Consequently, when this patient is confronted with a new problem, with unusual occurrences, or with strange, poorly perceived events, he may respond in erratic, rigid, or confused ways. He may then withdraw still further and reduce his range of activity in order to compensate for his limited ability to respond. Perception and performance are two phases of the same psychological process, and both depend upon what information is given and by what means communication takes place.

Substantive interventions. These interventions are intended to do something measurable for the aged and terminal patient, in addition to correcting reality testing and offering an opportunity for emotional expression. Even corrective measures include doing and saying something substantial that will fill in gaps and reaffirm connections with people and things. Aged people find it easy to slip away from reality, and reality soon passes them by. Instead of avoiding patients or silencing them with banal statements, such as, "Don't worry—everyone feels like that!" or "We've all got to go sometime!" the therapist should be trained to recognize situations that evoke the patient's vulnerability and to institute corrective measures. This can be facilitated by requiring attendants to make notes of deviant or irrelevant responses and to record exactly what the patient said or did in response to an unusual event. What is done *to* the patient is frequently a matter of record; what is done *for* the patient is not. It is even more important to know what is troubling a patient. Is he worried about an operation, a change in treatment, a new medication, or an omission of old medicine? Has he been preoccupied with his family, with the prospect of dying soon? The psychological autopsy has demonstrated how, in every case, various strands of behavior could have been drawn together in order to make up a coherent whole and, perhaps, even to devise a substantive intervention. Although it may be difficult to do anything to reverse or hold back the final illness, learning what a patient has felt or responded to in the terminal phase may, in itself, be a substantial contribution.

The distinction between these three types of intervention is one of emphasis, not of kind. Intelligent supervision helps the personnel to observe their own acts and to discover what acts patients respond to most effectively. Strategic participation by the personnel not only helps formulate treatment programs but requires no unusual expenditure of time. It is largely a problem of reassessment and organization in areas of treatment that have been underemphasized in the past.

THE TERMINAL PHASE
IN ITS SOCIAL CONTEXT

Should elderly people live apart from the rest of the community? There seems to be increasing acceptance—and promotion—of the doctrine that the welfare of our elders is best served when they are provided with special residential settings. The spectrum of these settings for the aged is quite broad. At one extreme we observe plush villages or apartment houses designed for the safety and convenience of elderly people who are otherwise free citizens in a milieu of age peers. At the other extreme we observe geriatric hospital units and other institutional facilities that are highly organized and routinized systems in which the aged live as patients or inmates.

The consequences of encouraging elders to live apart from their juniors has now become the subject of many investigations (e.g., Bennett & Nehemov, 1965; Rosow, 1967; Walkley, *et al.*, 1966). However, little attention has been given to the relationship between physical and social milieus and how the older person dies. We would expect appreciable differences in the terminal period among deaths that occur in a geriatric hospital, in other age-segregated settings, and in intergenerational contexts, such as at home or in general hospitals. We must assume that the range of environmental variation within one particular geriatric hospital is much smaller than the variation within the community at large. Yet the psychological autopsy series has taught us that even this limited range of variation can have significant implications for the manner in which the aged patient encounters death.

Some patients, for example, are transferred to a special setting within the hospital—the intensive treatment unit—when death is in prospect. Here they are likely to become still further isolated from the life of the institution by being placed in a side room. The transplantation from "home ward" to "death valley" becomes more than a change in physical environment; it marks a reduction in the variety and scope of the patient's social environment. He now is seen almost exclusively by medical and nursing personnel. Moreover, these are the specialists of the intensive treatment unit, not staff members with whom the patient has become at least casually familiar over the months or years. The boundaries between the patient and the world at large become decidedly less permeable. Other patients and staff members do not drop by, and the new setting is too busy and too formidable in its emotional salience. Relatives and other visitors from the outside sense that they are stepping into a very special location, a sort of "sacred space," as anthropologists might say. It seems required that visitors put on a special face before entering, walk softly, speak in hushed and respectful tones, be ever so careful about what is said and done in this realm. In the meantime, the ward personnel, well-adapted to the setting, move about briskly, confidently, dedicated to their specific tasks.

This description merely hints at the impact upon an elderly person when he is transferred from one setting to another, even when both settings are within the same institution. From individual cases, some of which have come to the psychological autopsy, more about the specific effects of changing the patient's environment has been learned. There was almost instantaneous psychological regression in some cases. When the patient eventually died, no one who was in his environment for the last weeks could report what, if anything, the patient had experienced, desired, or wished to communicate. In other cases, the investigators saw patients maintain a rich mental and emotional life until the last heartbeat. Sometimes the difference seems to depend upon simply the presence or absence of at least one person in the environment (usually a member of the nursing staff) who happened to have been well-acquainted with the patient before his condition worsened. Instead of seeing the new admission to the ward as just another sick, possibly terminal patient, the staff member who already knows the patient is able to offer an individual relationship as well as professional care. The nurse recognizes and respects this person for what he was before being undermined by illness—and the patient accordingly is given every opportunity to exercise his remaining social and intellectual resources, to communicate, to be a person.

When should an aged and possibly terminal patient be moved from one environment to another? What are likely to be the consequences? If the judgment is in favor of transfer, has adequate consideration been given to the timing? To the manner in which the move is to be made? To the purposes it is presumed to serve? Important decisions must be made in each individual case. Before pursuing this point, let us consider some of the social-context variables that influence the patient's well-being, apart from the prospect of transfer.

Dimensions of the Dying Situation

A comprehensive analysis of the total dying situation is beyond the scope of the present discussion. However, the list below indicates the direction a more intensive analysis might take. Each of the 12 questions pertains to a logically independent dimension of the social environment in which any aged person may find himself during his preterminal and terminal phases. These questions have been framed in such a way that each could be converted to one or more scales for environmental assessment.

1. To what extent is he being treated as an aged person?
2. To what extent is he being treated as a dying person?
3. To what extent is he being treated as a patient?
4. What is his social visibility as compared with its former state?
5. How permeable are the boundaries of his situation with respect to the larger community? Are the boundaries more permeable from one direction than the other?
6. How permeable are the various boundaries within the milieu?
7. To what extent is the milieu specialized?
8. To what extent is the milieu formalized and regulated?
9. To what extent is the milieu "pumped out" or enriched?
10. How central or peripheral is the role of the dying person within his milieu?
11. How flexible is the milieu in its accommodation to the characteristics of this particular person?
12. To what extent are transactions within the milieu monitored for educational and research purposes?

Each of these dimensions is illustrated below. Even this brief discussion should make it clear that the social context of the dying person is subject to many variations that may have important consequences for his well-being.

An aged and terminal person could find himself in an environment that is organized for geriatric care or for terminal care, but not for both. Or he might find himself in a situation unsuitable for either terminal or geriatric care. In any possible environment, however, it seems reasonable to expect that different priorities will be established and that a different order of practices will be carried out, according to the dominant emphasis. The psychological autopsy would be a useful method of studying these differences.

Patienthood is only one possible role for an aged terminal person. Although a terminal person usually has been diagnosed and treated by a physician, he is not automatically a patient in every dimension of the dying situation. He may, for example, be a father, an employer, a spouse, or, in retrospect, he may retain qualities of respect, fear, or antipathy. In a hospital situation, he might well be regarded primarily as a patient. But if the same man were in another social context, his patienthood might well recede into the background. He would simply be aged, or even considered to be dying, without necessarily being merely and entirely a patient.

Even within the hospital context, being a patient has a variety of meanings. On a surgical ward even a renowned scholar might be reduced to the status of his diseased organ. He would be, say, a carcinoma to his doctor, a complaining voice to his nurse, an open mouth to the dietitian, and an unpaid bill to the front office. Conceivably, there are other, equally extreme conditions in which the fact of dying might be almost incidental to the status of the person. To his wife, for example, or to his children, an aged, terminal person would remain more a total individual than simply a patient with a fatal illness.

One of the unfortunate consequences of placement in a milieu that is specialized—for dying, aging, or both—is reduced social visibility. This leads to further reduction in interpersonal transactions, so that the aged person suffers from isolation as well as from impoverished relations with other people. In contrast, some aged people living, or dying, for example, in the midst of an ethnic "melting pot" may achieve a place of honor and attention. The dying person may be placed near a window overlooking the street. Neighbors and friends gather around, visit, share food, give, and perhaps receive gifts. As a result, social visibility continues and may even be enhanced; there is no hardening of the barriers between the living and the dying.

The latter situation is quite different from the "death valley" atmosphere so often found in our institutions. Not uncommonly, communication within the milieu of the dying is so departmentalized that the staff members serving different specialties are almost impermeable to each other (Aring, 1966). Each follows his separate line of inquiry and practice, meeting with the others only on rare occasions.

A specialized environment for the dying is also likely to be formalized and regulated—high on the scale of institutional totality (Goffman, 1960). At its extreme, the formalized milieu is an impressively self-perpetuating system. Although much has been observed and written about high-totality situations in recent years, little attention has been given to implications for pre-terminal and terminal individuals. From the psychological autopsies and other studies the investigators have come to the conclusion that the full range of behavior and experience available to the dying person often is inhibited—unnecessarily—by the formalized-regulated model.

It is possible that the social context in which an elderly person is living out his final days could be specialized and formalized and still offer rich sensory and interpersonal stimuli. Aware that the dying person tends to be deprived of stimuli at many levels, those who are responsible for his milieu could enrich his life-space. This enrichment could take many forms, such as inclusion of items that are relevant to the particular individual and the development of what Lindsley (1964), in another context, has termed a "prosthetic environment." Most often, however, when we know that a milieu is specialized and formalized, we are safe in guessing that it also has been pumped out of stimuli that do not seem strictly necessary—the dying person's own clothes, almost all of his personal possessions, etc. The environment is stripped down to what is required for bare efficiency in surveillance, treatment, and housekeeping.

The dying person may or may not occupy a central role in his milieu. We ordinarily think of death in terms of the individual and suppose that he is certainly a most salient part of his situation. Yet there are many exceptions. War, disease, and disaster may strike large segments of the community. An elderly dying person may receive low priority both emotionally and functionally as the community struggles with general problems of survival and reconstitution. Again, in the terminal unit of a hospital that serves all age groups, the mere fact that one patient is dying does not compel special attention. The elderly person dying in such an environment is likely to be a "wallflower"; the younger and more appealing patients receive the most attention. When the terminal phase takes place in the household, the dying relative may be either isolated from the family's daily life or may become the pivotal concern.

It has been suggested that the milieu can be more or less flexible in its accommodation to the dying person. Some very important research problems are implicit here. In what ways and to what extent is it beneficial for the dying person to be called upon to accommodate *himself* to his situation? Is it possible that we might be performing a disservice in some instances if we try to adapt the environment to the person? What kinds of flexibility in the milieu can be most helpful? How can they be facilitated? The psychological autopsy method may provide many clues toward the solution of these problems, although other research procedures will also be required.

Research is the last of the 12 characteristics that have been proposed for analyzing the social context of dying. To what extent are transactions within the milieu monitored for educational and research purposes? "Not at all" or "very little" are the answers that would have to be given for most situations in which elderly people die, whether within an institution or outside. And so we learn almost nothing from the thousands and thousands of deaths that slip through us. We do not learn which procedures to preserve and which to modify or eliminate. Lacking hard data, as well as the critical attitude that accompanies investigation, we are likely to become stultified by unexamined tradition and cliché. Both formal and informal education occupy the same low estate as research. Those who inhabit the environments in which deaths occur usually do not learn much either from the patients or from each other.

Theoretically, each of these 12 characteristics of the dying situation can vary independently. For example, a specialized milieu could be either highly formal or informal, and a formalized milieu could be either pumped out or enriched, etc. In practice, however, many of these characteristics cluster together in predictable ways. Knowing that an aged person is in a preterminal or terminal condition and in a specialized environment, we can predict low social visibility, relatively impermeable boundaries, high formalization, stimulus deprivation, etc., which will lead to still further isolation.

What is the best explanation for the structure of the dying situation that prevails in our society? There are three possible explanations:

1. We have already hit upon the most satisfactory arrangement.
2. We, the living, have strong emotional needs to control the dying situation in this manner, whether or not it is truly in the best interests either of the terminal patient or society in general.

3. The social context of the dying situation has acquired its present form primarily from ideas and procedures that follow the line of least resistance, that is, from habits that have flourished without challenge or re-evaluation.

The first explanation is the least probable, and it might be prudent to reserve judgment about the other two possibilities until the social context of dying has been subjected to the intensive research it deserves. But it does seem relevant to repeat a recommendation that the authors made during a recent workshop on aging and death under the auspices of the Department of Health, Education, and Welfare. Essentially, this recommendation calls for the establishment of a multidisciplinary task force to (a) evaluate existing social and physical contexts in which deaths most frequently occur and (b) propose several alternative models. The alternatives presumably would range from modifications in already existing situations, such as chronic disease hospitals, to the development of entirely new settings or systems.

Problems that may arise when elderly and possibly preterminal patients are transferred from one context to another were touched upon earlier. Additional problems have been described elsewhere (Kastenbaum, 1966d). These include failure to prepare the patient adequately for the move, a lack of continuity of information and vital services from one setting to the next, insufficient care to ensure that further transfers will not be required, etc. Too frequently one encounters the ill and aged person who has been shunted from place to place as though he were an inaccurately addressed package. Yet the personnel who are involved in this process are not necessarily a hardhearted lot. It is probably closer to the truth to say that we possess very few adequate physical-social settings in which elders can pass through their terminal phases, perhaps due to the fact that we have given so little attention to conceptual models for the dying situation.

Fortunately, there are some settings—both home and institutional—in which the dying person and those around him share a rewarding experience. Cicely Saunders, Honorary Medical Director of St. Christopher's Hospice in London, England, has helped to develop an institutional milieu that favors the relief of suffering and the maintenance of dignity and self-respect during the terminal phase. She writes of "the achievements that people continually make in their dying. . . . Here we begin to see the moment which is fully personal, when everything is being finally summed up and the past is truly gathered together. . . . This is the moment of fullest individuality" (Saunders, 1966, p. 34). This statement, which stands in contrast to many of the observations reported in the present paper, serves as a reminder that it is possible to develop a social context that is truly sensitive and sympathetic to the needs of the dying person.

Social Diagnosis

One of the significant implications of the psychological autopsy is that, by finding out how to improve the social context for the terminal patient, we also improve the circumstances of the patient who has lived to an advanced age. The question of what kind of social context may be most beneficial cannot be decided solely on the basis of medical diagnosis. Appropriate placement and extended care depend upon *social diagnosis* as well. This means that, in addition to psychological evaluation and social casework study, many factors—not necessarily pathological—enter into the social diagnosis. For example, no social diagnosis would be complete without considering an aged person's ethnic background and his educational and economic status. Before he can be placed in a favorable social context, further attention should be given to his skills, customary way of life, capacities, interests, and vulnerability to stress. What, for example, do we know about how to diagnose individual life styles, patterns of social adaptation, resourcefulness, and so on? Mental status and economic potential are highly important, of course, but so are "life-expectancy ratings." However, these ratings should include, not only how long a doctor believes a patient will live, but what the patient himself can expect of life and what life, at this stage, defined by his immediate social situation, can reasonably expect of the patient.

Medical diagnoses are only part of the larger social context. The investigators have learned, from the psychological autopsies, that there are many older people who need neither the long-term custodial institution nor the short-term medical nursing home. They require different situations, corresponding to a variety of social diagnoses. Some people need extended care in a convalescent home; others require treatment in active rehabilitation centers, and still other people accommodate best in a loosely supervised community dwelling. Many mental hospitals have adapted to different clinical problems, a changing population, and evolving conceptions of psychiatric care (Cumming & Cumming, 1962). Certainly, the range of possible choices for the aged person who can no longer maintain himself in self-sufficient autonomy can be expanded too.

By studying the social problem of aging as well as dying, the psychological autopsy can shift its emphasis from the status of the patient who is in the terminal phase, or even the preterminal period, to the prevailing circumstances and social context of the patient prior to admission.

The concept of social diagnosis—which would include the medical diagnosis as well—is really a practical step, because most elderly patients are acutely ill only for brief periods and do not require prolonged, high-priority medical care. The significance of recent Medicare legislation only re-emphasizes the other needs and questions that should be investigated. How can the older person effectively advance and articulate himself within a society that has less and less place for him? Traditional medical care must be expanded in order to keep up with the urgency of appropriate social diagnosis.

MODIFICATION OF THE PSYCHOLOGICAL AUTOPSY FOR OTHER SETTINGS

The psychological autopsy need not be limited to geriatric patients. Shneidman and his colleagues (in press) have amply demonstrated the value of the psychological autopsy and the "death investigation team" in the study of suicide. Although their version of the psychological autopsy differs somewhat from this, both share several features in common. The key concept in both is to reconstruct the role that each person assumes in his own death. When studying suicidal people, the purpose is to ascertain whether the motive was intentional or subintentional, as opposed to unintentional participation. The psychological autopsy as used at Cushing Hospital also attempts to review, in perspective, the deceased person's life situation and tries to discover a reliable relationship between preceding events and the terminal illness. Both groups emphasize the correlation between psychosocial factors and death. However, the suicide study stresses the mode of death, whereas the psychological autopsy in the present investigation examines the precipitating events of the terminal period that led to illness and death. Both, however, share the viewpoint that the psychological autopsy is a useful and flexible method that can improve the resources of training and the treatment of patients.

The psychological autopsy format presented here could be introduced into many hospitals and medical facilities with relatively minor modifications. Most hospitals already have facilities for somatic post-mortem examinations. Indeed, to be accredited, hospitals must perform a substantial number of autopsies each year. Many hospitals also conduct "death conferences," so the staff can review the record of a recently deceased patient. Through the years, the clinico-pathological conference has become an essential part of medical education and postgraduate training. However, in the typical clinico-pathological conference, attention is given almost entirely to the disease, and there is scanty information about the patient who succumbed to that disease. This kind of death review puts considerable emphasis upon the physician's diagnostic acumen. The psychosocial concomitants of death are rarely discussed; as a result, the physician and his nonmedical colleagues are seldom left with an improved understanding of the patient "as a whole person."

When a patient is first admitted to a hospital, the staff is primarily concerned with establishing the diagnosis and treating the disease. When the patient dies, the cause of death is sought in the somatic autopsy, never in the social and emotional circumstances of the patient when he became sick. Hospital records are almost exclusively preoccupied with physical responses, anatomical lesions, and chemical data. Personal information is limited to social service reports and occasional psychiatric consultations.

Within existing hospital hierarchies, information is so stratified and responsibility so delegated that the physician who knows most about the disease is often least familiar with the circumstances in which his patient fell ill. He may, therefore, be equally uninformed about the social and emotional factors related to his patient's subsequent death. Furthermore, because he concentrates upon purely biological issues, he may assume that death and dying almost always can be thwarted, and he will tend to blame the advent of death upon technical error, therapeutic deficiency, or culpable ignorance.

The broad scope and multidisciplinary participation of the psychological autopsy can provide a nucleus for development of sustained concern with psychosocial factors, and with the preterminal patient as a human being. The investigators do not challenge the physician's traditional responsibility for life and death decisions, but they do urge that the substantial contribution of other staff members, who are no less concerned about the patient's welfare, be recognized. Curphey (1961) recognizes the contribution of the psychological autopsy to the work of the medical examiner in suicide. In a similar way, much more emphasis should be put upon social and psychiatric information when reviewing the deaths of medical and surgical patients. After all, dissection of the body is only one aspect of the somatic autopsy. Its value depends upon ample pre-mortem information. If somatic autopsies were performed without an adequate medical history, record of treatment, physical examination, or laboratory tests, post-mortems would be of little lasting value. If doctors did not offer objective information to the pathologist and, instead, made casual comments based only upon random impressions, the autopsy would forfeit its scientific value. Fortunately, however, physicians have been able to bring detailed, systematic observations to the post-mortem room, and the somatic autopsy and clinico-pathological conferences are therefore highly instructive exercises that check upon diagnosis, treatment, accuracy of tests, reliability of procedures, and results of management.

Frequent confrontations between members of various disciplines and specialties—medicine, nursing, psychology, social work, paramedical fields, and so forth—almost certainly will raise the standards of all levels of professional competence. This kind of mutual scrutiny exposes shortcomings, and no one wishes to appear remiss. How often do we know whether the social service department has thoroughly investigated the family's attitude and the circumstances of admission? What did the nursing staff think about the patient? How did the performance of the day and evening shifts differ? What kind of alliance did the house staff have with the patient and his family? How much communication was there with the referring physician? The psychological autopsy cannot answer questions that should have been asked when the patient was alive, but it can, assuredly, serve to ask questions, raise doubts, formulate fresh policies, and propose new avenues of investigation.

The format of the psychological autopsy may vary according to the circumstances and role of each institution. General hospitals, nursing homes, rehabilitation centers, and extended care facilities have different problems, personnel, and interests. To be effective in any institution, however, the psychological autopsy requires adequate information, zealous investigation of related questions, and reliable observations.

The choice of leader, or titular "pathologist," depends upon local circumstances. When a hospital has a strong psychiatric service, the psychological autopsy might well be structured as a logical extension of the psychiatric consultations to other services. In some hospitals, psychiatrists and other mental health specialists are employed on only a part-time basis. Any mental health professional who combines skill in leading group discussions with talent for organizing and evaluating psychological material might then be asked to familiarize himself with relevant literature and to preside. Under favorable circumstances, the psychological autopsy could be carried out by members of the medical or surgical staff. As a rule, this would require more interest and sophistication in psychological matters than most physicians have as yet been able to acquire. Demonstration groups, under the guidance of a competent consultant, could offer training in the psychological autopsy method. Consultants also might be made available for institutions that want to develop their own programs. It should be emphasized that the psychological autopsy should include a knowledgeable participant who is not involved in the day-by-day routine and policies of the institution. This person could provide valuable objectivity. Social psychologists, cultural anthropologists, and medical sociologists are some of the different kinds of guests who can offer substantial contributions.

Whether the setting is in a general hospital, a multiservice community agency, or an extended care facility, the psychological autopsy can be adapted to the specialized interests and problems of each. In one, there might be need to provide training for personnel who work with the terminally ill. In another, the emphasis might be upon the investigation of a specific disease, such as cancer, heart disease, stroke, or neurological illnesses. In still other settings, the administrative and physical aspects of caring for patients with chronic illnesses may need to be improved. In many situations, perhaps in all, the psychological autopsy may be structured primarily to decontaminate the taboo topic of death. The psychological autopsy has considerable potential as a means to improve the ways in which we determine the cause and circumstances of death. It can also be used by various specialists as a bridge into broader community health projects.

As death is relevant to everyone, but the exclusive property of none, the psychological autopsy provides an appropriate medium and common ground for workers with diversified training in medicine and science. Even beyond the medical field, careful examination may help those who work in many other areas to understand better the problems of death and dying.

VIII SUMMARY

Only in the recent past have systematic attempts been made to study the emotional and social processes of dying. There is very little known about what happens to aged men and women as they pass through the terminal phase of life. Assumptions and conjectures abound, but the lack of reliable information has delayed establishment of programs adjusted to the total care of the older person and has limited our understanding of the pressing needs of the dying patients.

In order to study the terminal phase of life from a perspective broader than that of medicine alone, the investigators have used a method of inquiry called the psychological autopsy. Essentially, the psychological autopsy is a multidisciplinary casework conference that is designed to draw together and correlate medical, social, and psychiatric information about a patient during the final period of his life. Its purpose is to complement the somatic autopsy, which seeks the immediate cause of death, by studying the psychosocial context in which death occurs. While reviewing the terminal phase of the patient's life against the background of his previous attitudes and modes of adaptation, the psychological autopsy has also determined how staff members respond to dying patients and how to evaluate different treatment programs.

The present report pertains to the first 80 patients in a series that now includes more than 120 recent deaths in a geriatric hospital. Their age at death ranged from 68 to 100, with a median of 83. About one-fourth of them died within the first year, and the remaining three-fourths died within five years. The median length of stay at the hospital was 31.5 months. Unlike patients in a general hospital, these patients were not, as a rule, acutely ill. Because they were in the hospital for such a long time, there was ample opportunity for the staff to become familiar with each patient's habits, relationships, and social visibility. In some cases, changes in attitude and behavior toward the end could be compared with earlier, "baseline" behavior. In other cases, however, it was found that some patients had always been "invisible" members of the hospital community. Very little more was known about them when they died than when they were admitted.

In order to review each patient as completely as possible, the investigation was divided into four stages, called the prehospital situation, hospital course, preterminal period, and final illness. The scope of the autopsy therefore extended from the circumstances leading to hospitalization and the patient's institutional adjustment and relationships, to the precipitating medical, social, and psychiatric events that initiated the lapse into terminal illness.

The study dealt also with each patient's social, ethnic, occupational, and economic background, his attitude toward hospitalization, and the medical diagnoses upon admission. A review of his hospital course emphasized how the patient got along with other people, including his relatives, visitors, and friends, as well as members of the staff and other patients.

The preterminal period received the most intensive study because the mental, social, and medical changes that occur just before the onset of the final illness have not been generally recognized as significant areas of in-

56

vestigation. Mental status, level of consciousness, and terminal symptoms were examined from the broad base of behavioral and interpersonal changes, not just as isolated medical events. Sometimes death was heralded by distinct emotional or social crises, and a few patients had a clear intimation that death was imminent.

The common assumption that old people progressively lose contact or interest in reality could not be substantiated. Most patients were in at least partial contact until almost the very end. In itself, this finding shows that the isolation imposed upon so-called terminal or even senile patients may not only be premature, but unwise. By assuming that aged or dying patients cannot respond to reality, the people who take care of them may inadvertently contribute to further alienation and impairment of reality testing.

Fear of dying was rarely observed and was met with only in patients who were grossly impaired. Because adequate communication could not be established, the apprehension these patients seemed to express might have been a response to defective reality testing, not to the awareness of impending death. Several patients talked about death apprehensively during periods of health but seemed to accept it during the preterminal period. In general, patients entering the terminal period could be separated into two groups. One group seemed to accept, and to be aware of, impending death. Most of these patients slipped into progressive withdrawal, refused to participate in their usual activities, and tended to remain as inactive as possible until the final illness. The other group was made up of patients busily engaged in everyday activities, making plans for the future, when they were interrupted by death.

The psychological autopsy points to many areas of potential research and offers a constant challenge to existing theories of aging. It has been noted that even having a weekly conference to discuss a recently deceased patient may have a salutary effect upon the staff. Because personnel may be called upon to report and to justify procedures, communication with terminal patients has improved. It has alerted nurses and aides to seek alternative ways to reach patients who had seemed inaccessible.

When we consider how important the somatic autopsy is to general medicine, the implications for the psychological autopsy seem almost overwhelming. Psychiatrists, psychologists, sociologists, social workers, and members of the nursing profession already have a mass of relevant observations that could help to improve the psychosocial context of the dying or aged patient. They need a place where they can exchange information and correlate observations with other physicians and members of the health professions. Hopefully, the psychological autopsy may also contribute to classification of behavior disturbances, which we have termed the "social diagnosis."

Tradition decrees that the physician is the arbiter who stands at the pinnacle of responsibility for patient care. As a general policy, especially when the patient is acutely ill, this cannot be disputed. There are many other instances, however, when the hierarchical structure of responsibility may demean the contributions to be made by other specialties and professions, no less devoted to the welfare of the patient. By further clarifying the social and emotional context of death and by formulating comprehensive social diagnoses for any patient who needs extended care, we may find that the medical diagnosis is only part of a broader viewpoint.

REFERENCES

ARING, C. D. Intimations of mortality: an appreciation of dying and death. Presented at the symposium on "Death in Medicine," Western Reserve University, Cleveland, Ohio, Sept. 27, 1966.

BENNETT, R., & NEHEMOV, L. Institutional totality and criteria of social adjustment in residences for the aged. *J. soc. Issues*, 1965, **21**, 44-78.

BEREZIN, M., & CATH, S. (Eds.). *Geriatric psychiatry: grief, loss, and emotional disorders in the aging process.* New York: International Univ. Press, 1965.

BLAUNER, R. Death and social structure. *Psychiat.*, 1966, **29**, 378-394.

BROMBERG, W., & SCHILDER, P. Death and dying. *Psychoanal. Rev.*, 1933, **20**, 133-185.

CHORON, J. *Modern man and mortality.* New York: Macmillan, 1964.

CHRIST, A. E. Attitudes toward death among a group of acute geriatric psychiatric patients. *J. Geront.*, 1961, **16**, 56-59.

CUMMING, J., & CUMMING, E. *Ego and milieu.* New York: Atherton Press, 1962.

CURPHEY, T. The role of the social scientist in the medico-legal certification of death from suicide. In E. Shneidman & N. Farberow (Eds.), *The cry for help.* New York: McGraw-Hill, 1961.

EGBERT, L., BATTIT, G., WELCH, C., & BARTLETT, M. Reduction of postoperative pain by encouragement and instruction of patients. *New Eng. J. Med.*, 1964, **270**, 825-827.

ERIKSON, E. Eight ages of man. *Amer. J. Psychiat.*, 1966, **2**, 281-307.

FEIFEL, H. Older persons look at death. *Geriatrics*, 1956, **11**, 127-130.

GOFFMAN, E. Characteristics of total institutions. In M. R. Stein, J. Vidich, & M. White (Eds.), *Identity and anxiety: survival of the person in mass society.* Glencoe, Ill.: Free Press, 1960.

HACKETT, T., & WEISMAN, A. Psychiatric management of operative syndromes. II: Psychodynamic factors in formulation and management. *Psychosom. Med.*, 1960, **22**, 356-372.

HENRY, J. *Culture against man.* New York: Random House, 1963.

HOMBURGER, F., & BONNER, C. *Medical care and rehabilitation of the aged and chronically ill.* Boston: Little, Brown, 1964.

JEFFERS, F. C., NICHOLS, C. R., & EISDORFER, C. Attitudes of older persons toward death: a preliminary study. *J. Geront.*, 1961, **16**, 53-56.

KASTENBAUM, R. The realm of death: an emerging area in psychological research. *J. hum. Relat.*, 1965, **13**, 538-552.

KASTENBAUM, R. On the meaning of time in later life. *J. genet. Psychol.*, 1966a, **109**, 9-25.

KASTENBAUM, R. Death as a research problem in social gerontology: an overview. *Gerontologist*, 1966b, **7**, 67-69.

KASTENBAUM, R. The mental life of dying geriatric patients. *Proc. 7th Internatl. Congress on Gerontology*, 1966c, V. 6, 153-159.

KASTENBAUM, R. Death and responsibility. I: overview. II: a critical summary. *Psychiat. Opin.*, 1966d, **2**, 5-7; 35-41.

KASTENBAUM, R. Multiple perspectives on a geriatric "Death Valley." *Community ment. Hlth. J.*, 1967, **3**, 21-29.

KASTENBAUM, R., & WEISMAN, A. The psychological autopsy as a research procedure in gerontology. In D. P. Kent, R. Kastenbaum, & S. Sherwood (Eds.), *Research, action, and planning for the aged: the power and potential of the social sciences.* New York: Behavioral Publications, in press.

KLOPFER, W. G. Attitudes toward death in the aged. Unpub. master's thesis, College of City of New York, 1947.

LIEBERMAN, M. Psychological correlates of impending death: some preliminary observations. *J. Geront.*, 1965, **20**, 181-190.

LIEBERMAN, M. Vulnerability to stress and the processes of dying. *Proc. 7th Internatl. Congress on Gerontology*, 1966, V. 8, 513-519.

LINDSLEY, O. R. Geriatric behavioral prosthetics. In R. Kastenbaum (Ed.), *New thoughts on old age.* New York: Springer, 1964. Pp. 41-60.

MUNK, W. *Euthanasia: or medical treatment in aid of an easy death.* London and New York: Longmans, Green, 1887.

MUNNICHS, J. *Old age and finitude.* Basel, Switzerland: Karger, 1966.

RHUDICK, P., & DIBNER, A. Age, personality, and health correlates of death concerns in normal aged individuals. *J. Geront.*, 1961, **16**, 44-49.

ROSENFELT, R. The elderly mystique. *J. soc. Issues*, 1965, **21**, 37-43.

ROSOW, I. *Social integration of the aged.* New York: Free Press, 1967.

SANDERSON, R. E., & INGLIS, J. Learning and mortality in elderly psychiatric patients. *J. Geront.*, 1961, **16**, 375-376.

SAUNDERS, C. A medical director's view of death. *Psychiat. Opinion*, 1966, **3**, 28-34.

SELYE, H. *The stress of life.* New York: McGraw-Hill, 1956.

SHNEIDMAN, E. S., & FARBEROW, N. (Eds.), *The cry for help.* New York: McGraw-Hill, 1961.

SHNEIDMAN, E. S. Orientations toward death: a vital aspect of the study of lives. *Internatl. J. Psychiat.*, 1966, **2**, 167-188.

SHNEIDMAN, E. S. Suicide: symptom of lethality. In C. Costello (Ed.), *Symptoms of psychopathology.* New York: John Wiley & Sons, in press.

SIMMONS, L. *The role of the aged in primitive society.* New Haven: Yale Univ. Press, 1945.

TALLAND, G. Performance studies in human aging and their theoretical significance. *Psychiat. Digest*, 1966, **27**, 37-53.

TITCHENER, J., ZWERLING, I., GOTTSCHALK, L., & LEVINE, M. Psychological reactions of the aged in surgery—the reactions of renewal & depletion. *A.M.A. Arch. Neurol. & Psychiat.*, 1958, **79**, 63-73.

WALKLEY, R. P., MANGUM, W. P., SHERMAN, S. R., DODDS, S., & WILNER, E. M. *Retirement housing in California.* Berkeley, Calif.: Diablo Press, 1966.

WALLACE, M. Speech therapy with geriatric aphasia patients. In R. Kastenbaum (Ed.), *New thoughts on old age.* New York: Springer, 1964. Pp. 161-178.

WEISMAN, A. Reality sense and reality testing. *Behav. Sci.*, 1958, **3**, 228-261.

WEISMAN, A. Discussion of suicide and appropriate death. *Internatl. J. Psychiat.*, 1966, **2**, 190-193

WEISMAN, A., & HACKETT, T. Predilection to death. *Psychosom. Med.*, 1961, **23**, 232-256.

WEISMAN, A., & HACKETT, T. The dying patient. *Forest Hosp. Publ.* 1962, 1, 16-21.

WOLFF, K. Personality type and reaction toward aging and death: a clinical study. *Geriatrics*, 1966, **21**, 189-92.

WORCESTER, A. *Care of the aged, the dying, and the dead.* Springfield, Ill.: Charles C Thomas, 1940 (2nd ed.).